MW00560121

Published by Bassline Publishing
www.basslinepublishing.com

All design and layout by Music Book Production Services
www.musicbookproductionservices.com

ISBN 13: 978-0-9926268-3-9

Notation Legend

The Stave: most music written for the bass guitar uses the bass clef. The example to the right shows the placement of the notes on the stave.

Tablature: this is a graphical representation of the music. Each horizontal line corresponds with a string on the bass guitar, with the lowest line representing the lowest string. The numbers represent the frets to be played. Numbers stacked vertically indicate notes that are played together. Where basses with five or six strings are required, the tablature stave will have five or six lines as necessary.

Notes shown in brackets indicated that a note has been tied over from a previous bar.

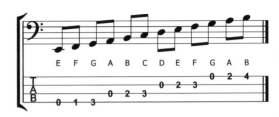

Repeats: the double line and double dot bar-lines indicate that the music between these bar-lines should be repeated. If the music is to be repeated more than once, a written indication will be given i.e. 'play 3x'.

1st & 2nd Time Endings: these are used for sections that are repeated, but which have different endings. The first ending is used the first time, the second is used on the repeat. The first ending is ignored on the repeat, only the second is used.

Slap: the note is slapped with the thumb.

Pop: the note is popped with either the first or second finger.

Thumb Upstroke: note is played with an upstroke of the thumb, usually following a slap

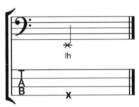

Left Hand: note is played by hammering on with the left hand.

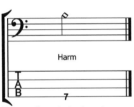

Harmonic: note is played as a harmonic by lighting touching the string above the fret indicated.

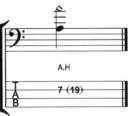

Artificial Harmonic: fret the lower note and tap the string over the fret shown in brackets.

Trill: alternate between the notes indicated by repeatedly hammering-on and pulling-off.

Vibrato: the pitch of the note is altered by repeatedly bending and releasing the string.

Hammer-On: only the first note is struck. The second is sounded by fretting it with another finger.

Pull-Off: Only the first note is struck. Lift the fretting finger to sound the second fretted note.

Slide: play the first note, then slide the finger to the second.

Right Hand Tap: note is tapped with a finger of the right hand. If necessary, finger will be specified.

Left Hand Tap: note is tapped with a finger of the left hand. If necessary, finger will be specified.

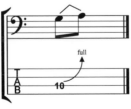

Bend: note is bent upwards to the interval indicated. ½ = semitone, full = tone.

Bend and Release: note is bent up to the interval indicated then released to the original note.

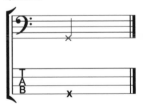

Ghost Note: note is a pitchless 'dead' note used as a rhythmic device.

Accent: note is accentuated, or played louder.

Staccato: note is played staccato - short.

Tenuto: note is held for its full length.

p   *piano* - played very softly
mp   *mezzo-piano* - played moderately quietly
f   *forte* - played loud/strong
mf   *mezzo forte* - played moderately loud/strong

D.C al Coda: Return to the beginning of the song and play until the bar marked Coda. Then jump to the section marked Coda.
D.S al Coda: Return to the sign, then play until the bar marked Coda. Then jump to the Coda.
D.C (or D.S) al Fine: Return to the point specified, then play until the Fine marking. Stop at this point.

Contents

Introduction

Welcome to *Advanced Studies for Bass Guitar,* the fourth book in the Bass Techniques Series. This book contains ten study pieces that will provide you with an opportunity to refine and build on the technical side of your playing. All of the techniques required by the contemporary electric bass player are covered here, from fingerstyle and plectrum playing, to slap bass and two handed tapping. There are also pieces that will allow you to focus on your chordal and harmonic playing.

The pieces in this book are study pieces, or 'études', meaning that they have been written to allow you to focus specifically on either a technique, or a musical idea. As the title of the book suggests, these are challenging pieces, meaning that it's important for you to have a solid grasp of the technique in question before working on them. Each one should be studied carefully, practised slowly and perfected over time. Once you have mastered a piece, you will have attained a high level of skill with that particular technique.

I wrote this book for a number of reasons, chief amongst these the fact that as a teacher I am often asked by my students to recommend study pieces that will help them focus on specific techniques. With that in mind, I realised that over my many years of playing the bass, I had accumulated a number of short pieces of my own that I use for keeping my 'chops' in shape. Some of these I had been keeping on the back burner with the idea that I might turn them into full-length songs at some point, but realising that one of my main musical strengths is as an educator rather than as a composer, I decided instead to treat them as study pieces. I also took the opportunity to use the writing of this book as a way to force myself to finish developing some ideas that I had been intermittently working on for several years! The result is this book: a collection of ten studies that will provide you with plenty of musical challenges as you work to improve your technical abilities.

For each piece you will find a set of detailed performance notes. These will help you with difficult fingerings and provide advice when tackling some of the technical aspects of the study. If you require further help with any of the techniques themselves, the other books in the Bass Techniques series - *Ultimate Slap Bass, Ultimate Tapping for Bass Guitar* and *Plectrum Technique for Bass Guitar* are the perfect place to start. All three are also available from Bassline Publishing. For each piece I have also included a recommended listening list which references compositions by well-known bass players that will serve as excellent additional study material. Listening to and analysing these great songs will reinforce your studies significantly. If you have the time and patience to transcribe and learn them as well, this will be of even greater benefit to you!

Audio Files

All of the study pieces in this book come with an accompanying audio file to listen to and where appropriate a full-band backing track. All of the required audio files can be downloaded FREE from the Bassline Publishing website. To find the audio, simply log in to your account and click on the Free Stuff! link on the main menu. You'll find the audio files in a zip folder listed with the bonus content for this book. Right click and select 'Save as' to download.

I'd like to thank a few people for their help and support during the writing of this book, first and foremost the superb musicians that played on the recordings: Dan Goldman (keys), Jamie Hunt and Stuart Ryan (guitars), James Hester (drums) and James Uings for his advice and assistance with mixing and mastering the audio. I'd also like to thank Joel McIver at Bass Guitar Magazine, Corey Brown at NoTreble.com, Nick Wells at iBass Magazine, Joe Zon for his amazing basses, Dave Avenius at Aguilar, Adrian Ashton at Mansons Guitar Shop, all of my private students and of course all of my students past and present at BIMM Bristol. Finally, I'd like to thank my wife Laura for the fantastic cover design, as well as her continued love and support.

I hope that you enjoy the pieces in this book and that they help you in your journey towards mastering the bass guitar. As ever, I would be delighted to hear your thoughts, as well as answer any questions that you might have. You can email me at stuart@basslinepublishing.com.

Stuart Clayton
December 2014

Fingerstyle Study No. 1

This piece is the first of two that will allow you to work on your fingerstyle playing. It has a slow tempo and features a busy semiquaver-based line that is challenging to play accurately. It's also a great work-out for tightening up your fretting hand fingerings and strengthening any fingers that might be weak.

The opening A section is the main theme of this study and is used at several points throughout the piece. The actual bassline begins with an E semiquaver at the end of the two bar drum intro. This note is an 'anticipation' and is played on the final semiquaver subdivision of the beat - the 'a' if you use the popular semiquaver vocalistion *1-e-&-a*. There is then a semiquaver rest at the beginning of the first bar of the main groove, with the line proper then starting on the second semiquaver. The first half of the first bar relies heavily on notes from the E minor pentatonic scale and walks downwards to an A at the end of the third beat. It then moves chromatically down to G during the first beat of the second bar. You will probably find it easiest to play the line so far using condensed fingering in the fretting hand - this is the system of covering a three-fret stretch with four fingers and is often used on the bass guitar.

TIP!

If you want to learn more about semi-quavers and how to count them, be sure to check out The Bass Guitarist's Guide to Reading Music: Intermediate Level, *also available from Bassline Publishing.*

The remainder of the second bar is devoted to a turnaround phrase that ends with the same E that was used as the anticipation at the beginning of the piece. This two bar line is then repeated twice more. The line then begins again for a fourth time, but this time climaxes with a fill (bar 6) to end the section. When playing this, I recommend that you now use the finger-per-fret method (see photograph on the next page) to cover frets two to five - this will enable you to play all of the notes in this phrase in one position. When playing this first section of the piece, try to keep all notes as staccato as possible - this will really help with the feel.

The line at letter B is essentially the same as the one from letter A, but with some added fills the second and fourth time through the two-bar sequence. For the fill on the second time through (bar 10), I recommend playing the E at the seventh fret of the A-string in the bar before with your first finger and then using the finger-per-fret method to cover the seventh to tenth frets. Again, this will enable you to play the entire fill in one hand position, which should make the line much smoother. This section ends with a more elaborate fill (bar 14) that is played as follows: use your first finger for the A at the end of the previous bar. This will then allow the second finger to play the Bb and the fourth finger to easily play the G on the A-string. After playing the ascending A-A#-B phrase with the first three fingers, you will need to perform a quick position shift, placing the first finger on the D at the twelfth fret of the D-string. You can then play the next group of three ascending notes (D-D#-E) in this position. The final double stop sequence can either be played with a barre or with the first and second fingers on the E and A respectively. Whichever you chose, simply slide upwards a fret at a time to play the remaining two double stops.

A new line begins at letter C. Like the previous section, this part begins with a semiquaver rest, after which a quicker line is played using some demisemiquavers. Although these look difficult on paper, the relatively slow tempo will make them a little easier to perform than you might expect. Note that the first three notes of the sequence are played as a hammer-on, so the picking hand only has to play the string once. The fretting hand should fret the C# with the first finger, allowing all of the remaining notes to fall into place using the finger-per-fret system. The second and third bars of this section are identical aside from the final two notes being played an octave lower in the second bar. The fourth bar features another long fill - play this by starting with the first finger of your picking hand on the C# at the sixth fret of the G-string. This will enable you to cover all of the notes within the first beat with one hand position. At the beginning of the second beat, fret the B with the fourth finger, then immediately move that finger down one fret so that your hand is covering frets five to eight. This will enable you to play the remainder of the line using the finger-per-fret method. Listen closely to the audio for guidance when learning this part.

ADVANCED STUDIES FOR BASS GUITAR

At letter D, the earlier part from letter B is reused. The only difference this time around is the final fill, which this time adds an additional double stop of G and C to the end. This sets up the transition into the next section.

At letter E a new line begins, accompanied by a new key signature, F. This reflects the C^{13} chord that underpins this line. The bass begins with a sliding double stop figure that begins on A and D$^\sharp$ - at the seventh fret of the D-string and eighth fret of the G-string respectively - then slides up a semitone to B♭ and E. The B♭ and E are the flattened seventh and major third of the C^{13} chord, making this a use of the classic 'funk double stop' that is commonly found in funk basslines. After this phrase, the line drops to the low E and then plays a chromatic ascending line, bouncing off of the open E-string on the way. On the final beat of the first bar, a hammer-on is played from G to A and then followed with two C's. These notes again reinforce the tonality. The next bar (bar 28) is similar, but this time the funk double stop is inverted and played higher up on the neck. The E is now in the lower position - at the fourteenth fret of the D-string - and the B♭ is on top, at the fifteenth fret of the G-string. Again, these notes are preceded by the notes a semitone below, which slide up into them. Note that whichever way around the funk double stop is played, the interval between the two notes is always a tritone, or flattened fifth. This interval adds tension, but sounds great because it uses the two strongest notes in the dominant chord (the major third and the flattened seventh). This two-bar line is played four times, and in the final bar (bar 30) the funk double stop is played a semitone lower, to reflect the B^7 chord. This serves as a perfect cadence back into the original key. The final section of the piece - letter F - is a repeat of the earlier B section.

When performing this study the trick is to relax and ensure that you do not push the beat. You should be playing 'on' the beat rather than ahead or behind. As stated earlier, keeping the majority of the notes in the 'Chorus' sections (at letters A, B, D and F) nice and short will help the piece groove.

Sound Advice

I recorded this piece using my Zon Sonus 4-string bass. I used both pickups, favouring the neck pickup slightly. I plucked the strings

The 'Finger-per-fret' Technique

between the two pickups, which allows for a tight sound that still retains enough bottom end. Playing position is very important to lines such as this - you'll get a tighter, but thinner sound the further back towards the bridge you move your hand and a fuller, fatter sound the closer you get the end of the neck. In my opinion, playing between the pickups is essentially the best of both worlds.

Recommended Listening

1. 'Opus Pocus' - Jaco Pastorius
2. 'Stratus' - Billy Cobham (Lee Sklar on bass)
3. 'You Got to Funkifize' - Tower of Power (Rocco Prestia on bass)
4. 'Barbary Coast' - Weather Report (Jaco Pastorius on bass)
5. 'The Chicken' - Jaco Pastorius
6. '4AM' - Herbie Hancock (Jaco Pastorius on bass)
7. 'I Can Dig It Baby' - Little Beaver (Jaco Pastorius on bass)
8. 'New Funk' - UZEB (Alain Caron on bass)
9. 'PAC Man' - Alain Caron
10. 'Past Lives' - Level 42 (Mark King on bass)

Fingerstyle Study No. 1

Written by Stuart Clayton

ADVANCED STUDIES FOR BASS GUITAR

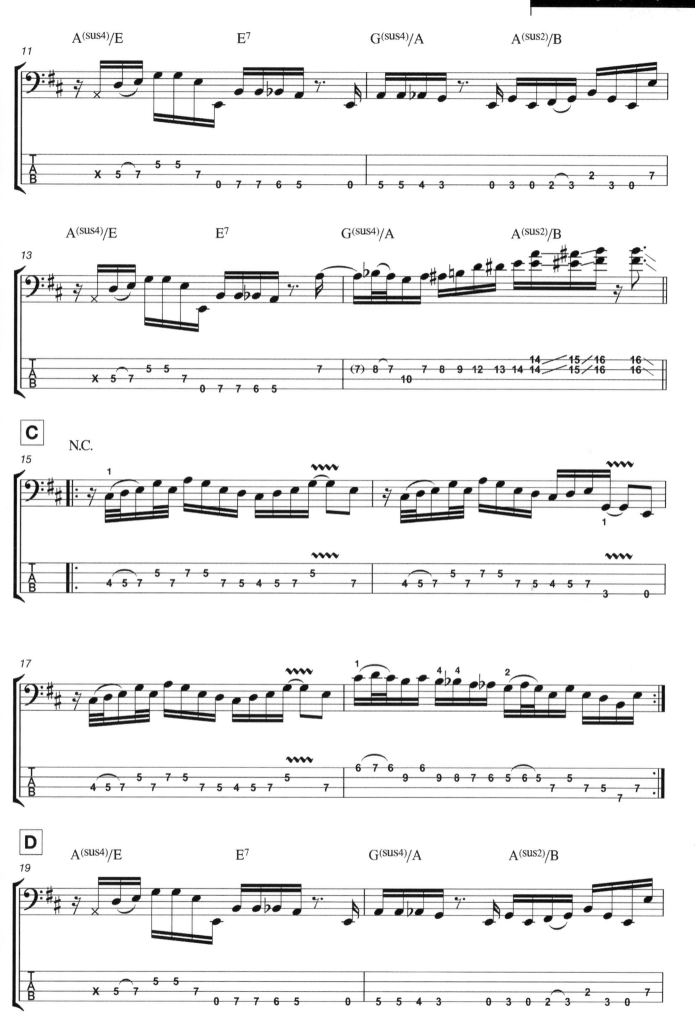

ADVANCED STUDIES FOR BASS GUITAR

Fingerstyle Study No. 2

This second fingerstyle study has a very quick tempo and features the kind of fast-paced fingerstyle grooves that were made popular by legendary bassists such as Jaco Pastorius and Rocco Prestia. There are also some chordal parts and tricky unison lines to get your fingers around, making it a very challenging piece to master. This study will also serve as a great workout for the fretting hand and will certainly put your use of the finger-per-fret method to the test.

The Intro, at letter A, is played at a slower tempo to the rest of the piece and features some double stop chords and simple melodic phrases in the bass. For each bar/chord, the bass plays a root note - which is held throughout the bar - and a simple phrase above it. The best way to perform this section is to pluck the lower notes with the thumb of the picking hand and play the melodic lines with the first and second fingers. In order to keep the bass notes ringing beneath the melodic phrases, you will need to closely follow the fretting hand fingerings that are written on the notation stave. Some of these chords, such as the F chord in bar 9 are difficult to move to quickly. In this instance, you'll need to fret the F at the eighth fret of the A-string and the C at the tenth fret of the D-string with the second and fourth fingers respectively, leaving the first finger free to fret the D at the seventh fret of the G-string. The third finger can then be used for the hammer-on to the E at the ninth fret of the G-string.

At letter B, the tempo jumps to 120bpm and the bass plays a tricky unison line with the keyboards. This section is a real tip-of-the-hat to 'Spain' by Chick Corea, which utilises similar ideas. When performing this section, pay close attention to note duration: the rests must be played as rests and any notes marked staccato should be played as such. The finger-per-fret method is recommended throughout this line and all of the fingerings added above the notation reflect this advice. When playing the opening phrase, the second finger should fret the notes at the twelfth fret as stated on the score: you'll need to barre across with this finger in order to play the D at the twelfth fret of the D-string (see photograph on the opposite page). You'll use the same technique to play the notes at the fourteenth fret. In the second bar of this line (bar 14) you should move your hand down one fret in order to start the

phrase on the fourth finger. This phrase is tough to play using the finger-per-fret method as it focuses heavily on the third and fourth fingers, but this will be a great workout for your fretting hand. Remember that tricky phrases such as this should be practised slowly and out of tempo in order to allow your fingers the time needed to become comfortable with the required movement. The repeat of this line leads into the main groove section at bar 19.

The bassline that begins at bar 19 is a semiquaver-based samba-style groove similar to those played by bassists such as Jaco Pastorius and Stanley Clarke. This continuous line sounds difficult to perform (it's certainly not easy) but is made more manageable through the use of hammer-ons. Be sure to play these where written as they will really help with both the execution and the feel of the line. This part is essentially a one-bar groove, with a slightly different phrase in the second bar. This two-bar pattern is played three times then gives way to another two-bar unison line that is played with the keyboards. After playing the hammer-on from A to B at the beginning of the fourth beat, you'll need to perform a quick position shift to place your first finger on the D at the twelfth fret of the D-string for the remainder of the phrase. The line is then a descending series of third intervals capped with a turnaround lick at the end of the second bar.

At letter C the melody section of the piece begins, underpinned by the same bass groove. There is a fill in the fourth bar of this sequence (bar 26) that is best played using the finger-per-fret method. You'll need to use your second finger to barre across the fifth fret to play the D and G notes at the fifth fret at the end of this bar.

At bar 31 the chord changes to A[7] and bassline alters accordingly. All of the hammer-on figures here are approaches to chord tones: the F# to the G is an approach to the seventh of the chord (G), the D to E is an approach to the fifth (E), and the C to C# is an approach to the major third. All of these figures are extremely common in lines such as this and you will encounter them often in your career as a bass player. The fourth bar of the A[7] section (bar 32) is a turnaround bar, after which the line begins again. This time the chord moves to C[Δ7] after two bars, beginning the final part of this section of the piece. The bassline used here is a typical funk/latin groove similar to some of the lines played by Stanley Clarke on 'Spain'. The section ends with a one-bar figure that is a quote from the beginning of the unison line at letter B, played an octave lower. Following this, the main bass groove begins again for two bars, before the two-bar unison riff is performed again.

At letter D the piano solo begins, underpinned by the same fingerstyle groove. This time around however there are are several variations on this playing of the line. A different fill is used in the fourth bar (bar 46) and this is again best played with the finger-per-fret technique. If you are not comfortable using this fretting technique at quick tempos, you will find fills like this challenging. If that's the case, remember that this is point of study pieces and work on this bar slowly and carefully in isolation until you have mastered it. There is a second fill which requires an explanation in this section, this time at bar 54. This fill uses chromatic passing notes to approach chord tones from the A^7 chord. If you play the B in the first beat with your first finger on the fourth fret on the G-string, the remainder of the line should fall into place using the finger-per-fret method. This section has a slightly different ending, with two bars of F$^{\triangle 7}$ replacing the unison line that was used before.

The final section of this study is a repeat of the earlier unison melody.

Good luck with this piece. The groove sections are tough to play at this tempo, but by following the advice above - particularly with regard to fingerings and the use of hammer-ons, you should find that it comes together a little easier than you might think. The most important thing is that you practise the parts slowly - you can gradually increase the tempo in small increments as you become more comfortable with the line.

Sound Advice

I performed this track using my Zon Sonus 5-string bass. I favoured the bridge pickup slightly and the EQ on the bass was set flat. Some EQ adjustments and a small amount of compression was added digitally once the part was recorded.

A 'barre' across
the strings

Recommended Listening

1. 'What is Hip' - Tower of Power (Rocco Prestia on bass)

2. 'Oakland Stroke' - Tower of Power (Rocco Prestia on bass)

3. 'Spain' - Chick Corea & Return to Forever (Stanley Clarke on bass)

4. '(Used to be a) Cha Cha' - Jaco Pastorius

5. 'Come On, Come Over' - Jaco Pastorius

6. 'Port of Entry' - Weather Report (Jaco Pastorius on bass)

7. 'Kuru/Speak Like a Child' - Jaco Pastorius

8. 'PAC Man' - Alain Caron

9. 'The Chinese Way' - Level 42 (Mark King on bass)

10. 'Hit Me with Your Rhythm Stick' - Ian Dury & The Blockheads (Norman Watt-Roy on bass

Fingerstyle Study No. 2

Written by Stuart Clayton

ADVANCED STUDIES FOR BASS GUITAR

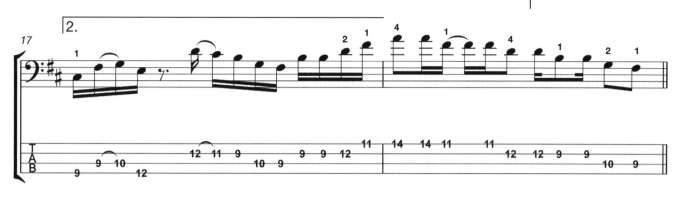

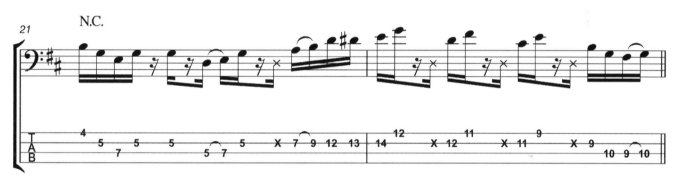

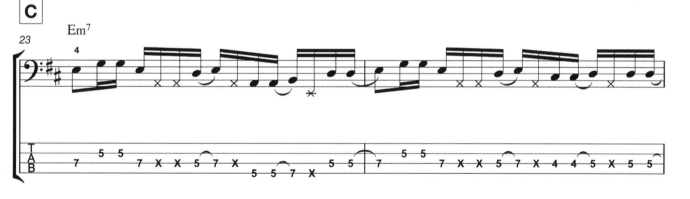

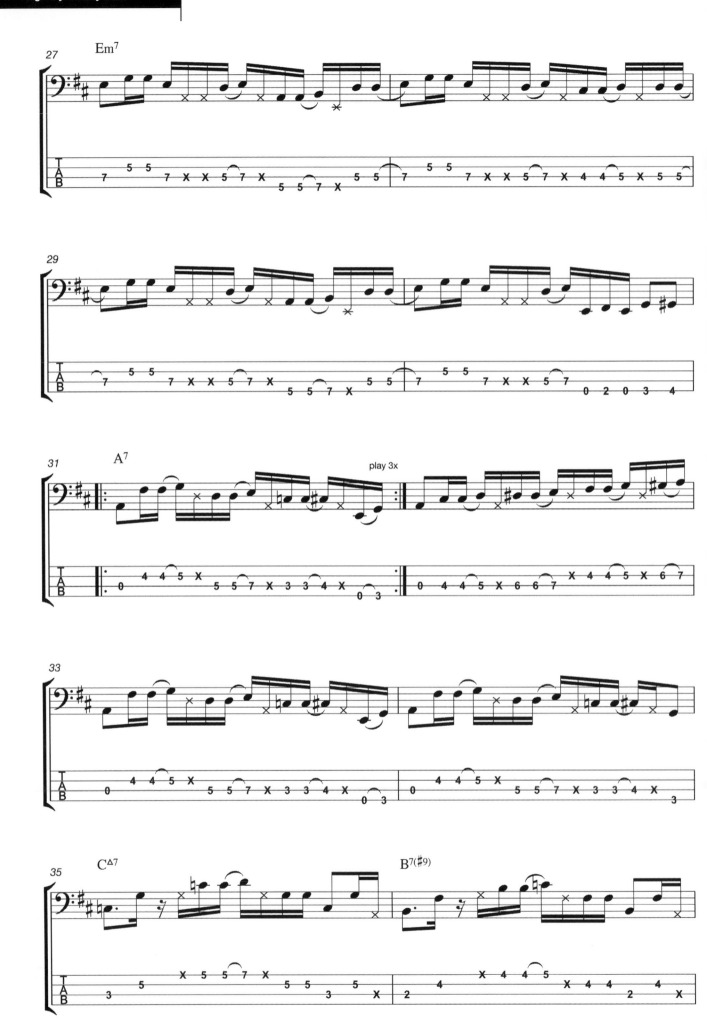

ADVANCED STUDIES FOR BASS GUITAR

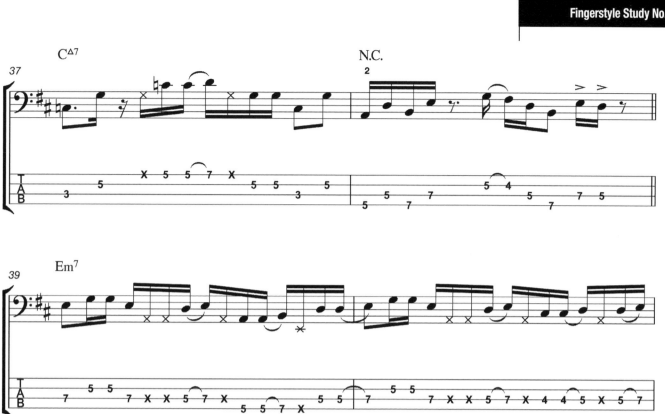

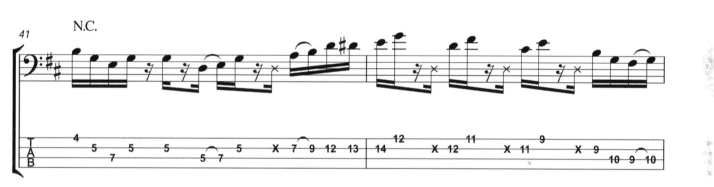

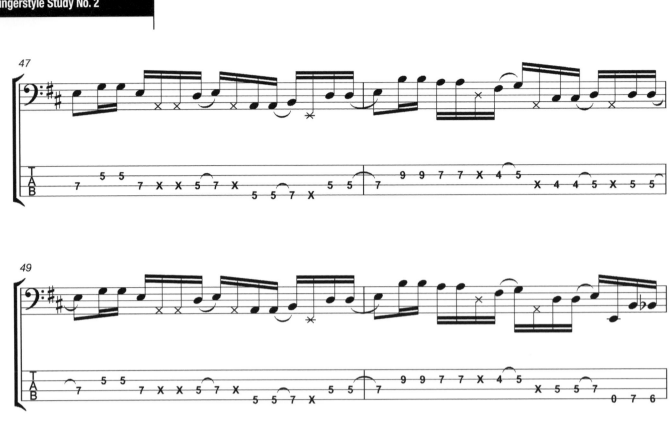

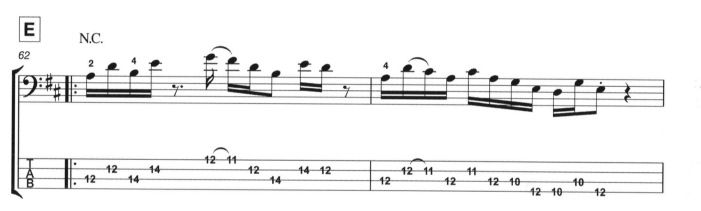

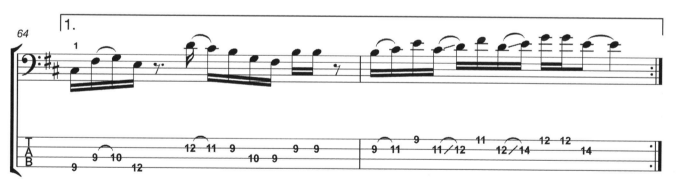

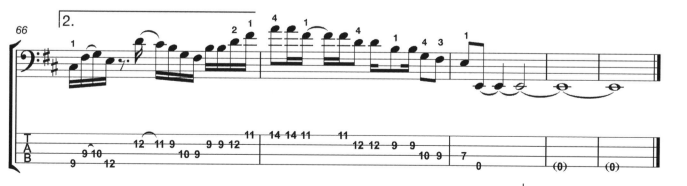

Chordal Fingerstyle Study

This piece requires the use of the chordal fingerstyle technique, where the thumb, index and middle fingers of the picking hand are used in the same way that a classical guitarist might play an acoustic guitar (shown in the photograph on the opposite page). This technique is quite often used by bass players as well, making it a nice tool to have under your belt.

The opening section of this piece at letter A outlines a series of upper register chords in the key of E minor. For each chord, the top two notes - E and B, played at the fourteenth fret of the D-string and the sixteenth fret of the G-string respectively - remain the same. As the bass notes change beneath them, these notes take on a different function within the chord: in Em they are the root and fifth, in C$^{\triangle 7}$ the major third and major seventh, and in Am^{add9} they are fifth and the added ninth. I recommend that you fret these two notes with the first and fourth fingers. You can then fret the C and G bass notes with the second finger. The F$^{\sharp}$ bass note at the end of the second bar should also be fretted with the second finger. When playing this section, be sure to allow the notes to ring into one another, creating a chordal effect.

At letter B a new part is introduced. When playing this, fret the E on the A-string with the first finger of the fretting hand and the B with the third. This will allow you to easily play the C on the third beat with the fourth finger. The C$^{\triangle 7}$ chord at the end of the bar should be fretted as follows: fret the C with the second finger, the E with the first and the B with either the third or fourth. You can then move this hand position downwards to play the G$^{\triangle 7}$ chord in the following bar. This two-bar motif is played four times.

At letter C a similar melodic line is played, this time beginning on an A minor chord. When playing this part, it makes sense to fret the C at the tenth fret of the D-string with the second finger, and the E at the ninth fret of the G-string with the first. This leaves the third and fourth free; the third can be used to play the F$^{\sharp}$ and the fourth can play the G. When playing the C chord in the following bar (bar 18), it is recommended that you fret it as follows: fret the C on the E-string with the first finger, the E on the G-string with the second and the C on the D-string with the third - the reason for fretting this chord in this way will be clear by the end of the section. At the end of bar 22, this C chord is

arpeggiated and the voicing is moved upwards to a D chord at the beginning of bar 23. The E minor chord that follows can be played in one of two ways: you can either use your first finger to barre across the twelfth fret to hold down both the E and G, or you can fret each note individually with the first and second fingers respectively. Either way, the third finger should be fretting the E at the fourteenth fret of the D-string, leaving the fourth finger free to perform the hammer-on from G to A and back again. This section ends with a nice voicing of an F$^{\triangle 7\sharp 11}$ chord: fret the F with the first finger, the E with the second, the C with the third and the top B with the fourth. This is a tricky fingering to switch to quickly, but it is the most logical for the chord. Note the crescendo as this chord is repeatedly arpeggiated - try to build the volume and intensity here before dropping back to a quieter level for the next section, which is a repeat of the Intro part.

Section D is very similar to the B section, but with some additional voicings added to keep things interesting. The first of these is the voicing of the G$^{\triangle 7}$ chord in bar 35. Fret the G with the first finger, the F$^{\sharp}$ with the second and the B with the third. This will leave your fourth finger free to play the C that follows it. The next new voicing is again for the G$^{\triangle 7}$ chord, this time in bar 39. The voicing itself will be familar, but this time you should take care to fret the this chord using the first three fingers, leaving the fourth free to play the higher G that follows it.

Section E is an embellished version of the earlier line from section C. This time there are some decorations to perform (at bars 42 and 44). These should be played legato: pluck the string only once and perform each sequence of notes using hammer-ons, pull-offs and slides, as written. The fingerings for these decorations are included above the notation and should be followed closely since they are the most effective fingerings for performing them. This part is followed by another repeat of the Intro chord sequence, which this time segues into a new part, at letter F.

At letter F, you will mostly be playing off of the open A-string. The first voicing - for the A minor chord - should be played with the first finger of the fretting hand on the G and the fourth on the E. This fingering can then be moved downwards two frets for the F^6/A chord. The turnaround at the end of this four-bar sequence is tricky to play as the chords

The Chordal
Fingerstyle Technique

move quickly: for the Am⁷ chord, fret the E with the first finger and the C with the fourth finger. For the G⁷ chord, fret the G with the first finger, the F with the second and the top B with the third. This chord is followed by the F△7#11 chord which should be fretted using the same fingering as described earlier. The final chord is a G: fret the G with the first finger, then use the third to fret the C, pulling-off to sound the B with the second finger - this second finger will already need to be in place before you play the pull-off. The final G is fretted with the third finger. As already noted above, the difficulty here is changing chord voicings quickly, something that bass players are not typically called upon to do.

The remaining sections of this piece are repeats of earlier parts.

This piece was written back in 2006 and might be familiar to those of you who have read *Solo Arrangements for Electric Bass*, also available from Bassline Publishing. Although a relatively simple piece, it has been very popular amongst my students and has been used on several occasions as an exam or audition piece.

Sound Advice

I performed this piece using my GB Rumour 4-string bass. I played with my picking hand position in between the two pickups where I have a ramp installed to decrease the distance between the strings and the body surface. This makes the application of certain techniques such as chordal fingerstyle playing a little easier. You can see an example of a ramp in the photograph above. I used both pickups equally and left the tone controls set flat. Some minor EQ adjustments were also made digitally, where a small amount of compression and reverb were also added. When performing this piece yourself, I recommend using the same pickup and tone settings and adding a little reverb or chorus if possible - either will enhance the chordal nature of the piece and will make performing - and listening to it - more enjoyable.

Recommended Listening

1. 'Hours by the Window' - Level 42 (Mark King on bass)

2. 'Blackbird' - Jaco Pastorius

3. 'Nostalgia' - GHS (Stuart Hamm on bass)

4. 'November' - GHS (Stuart Hamm on bass)

5. 'The Lesson' - Victor Wooten

6. 'NV43345' - Talas (Billy Sheehan on bass)

7. 'Sex in a Pan' - Bela Fleck & the Flecktones (Victor Wooten on bass)

8. 'Sammy Says Ouch! - Randy Coven

9. 'Meditation in E' - Zander Zon

10. 'Looking Glass' - Zander Zon

Chordal Fingerstyle Study

Written by Stuart Clayton

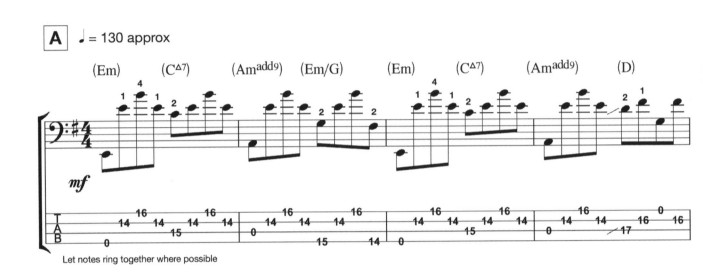

Let notes ring together where possible

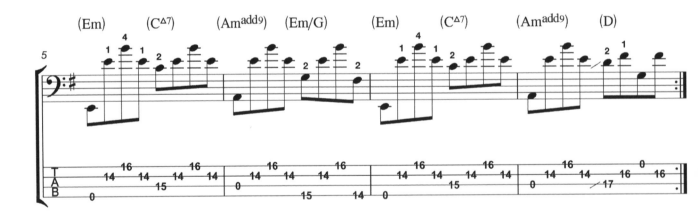

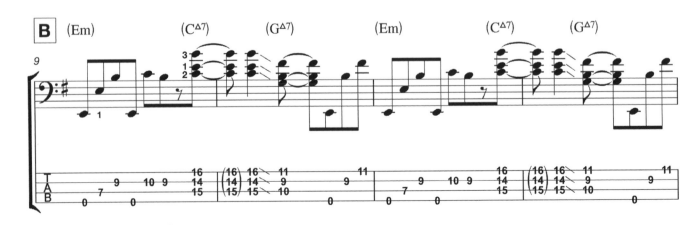

ADVANCED STUDIES FOR BASS GUITAR

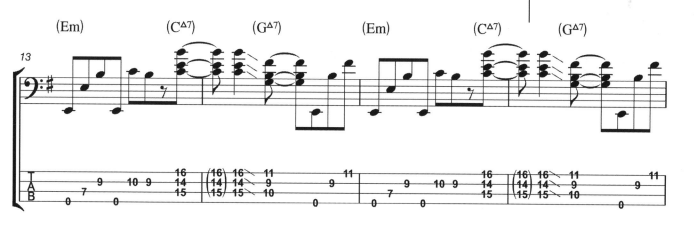

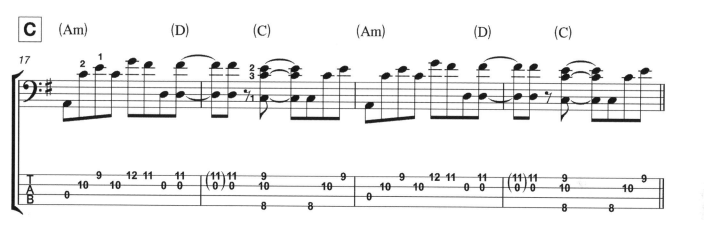

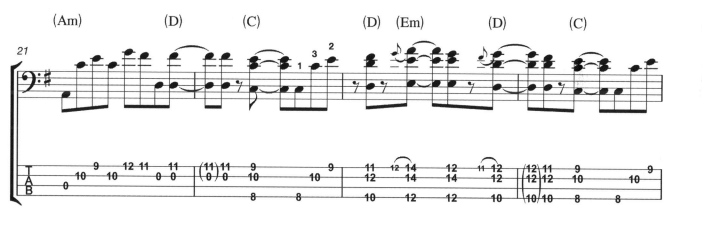

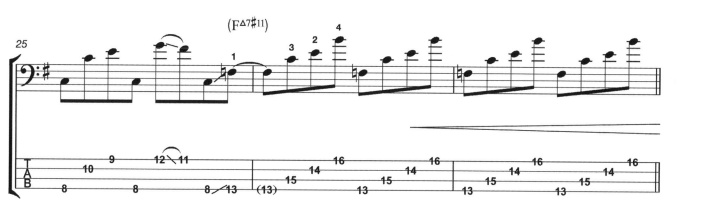

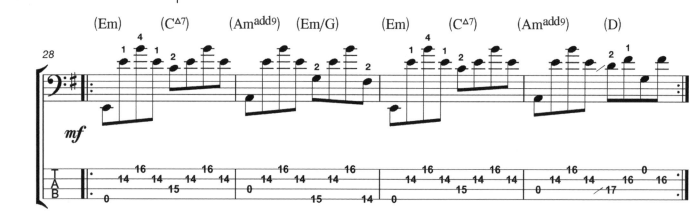

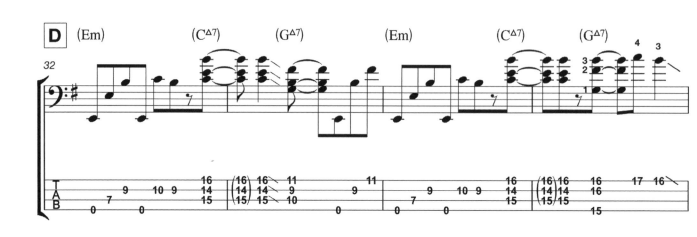

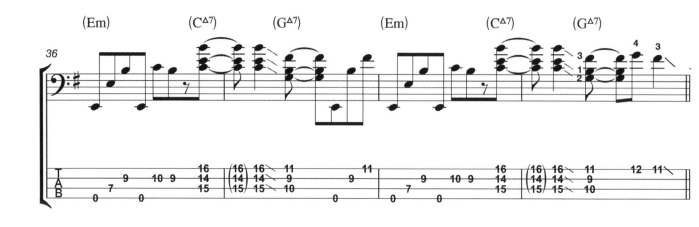

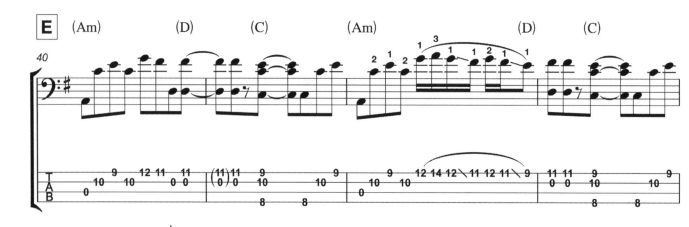

ADVANCED STUDIES FOR BASS GUITAR

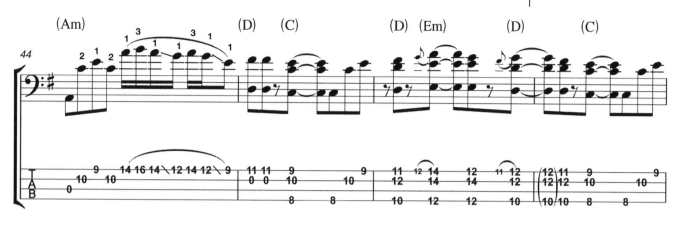

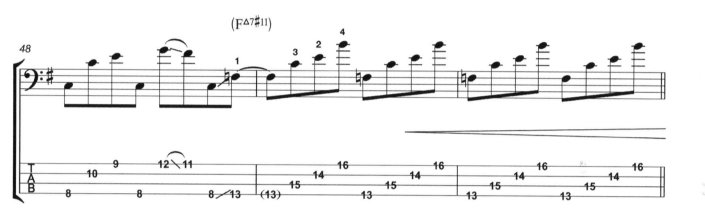

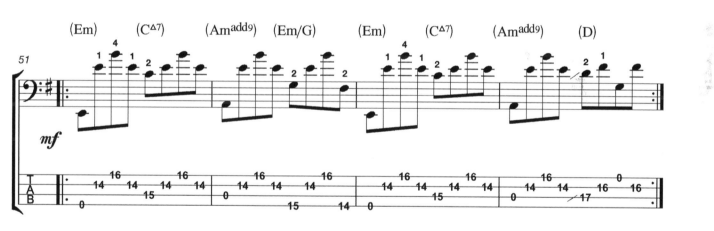

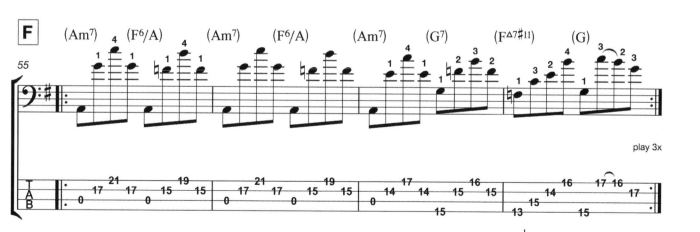

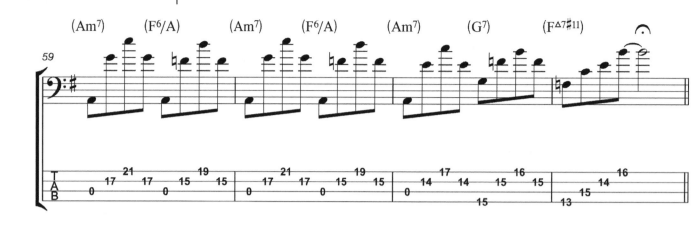

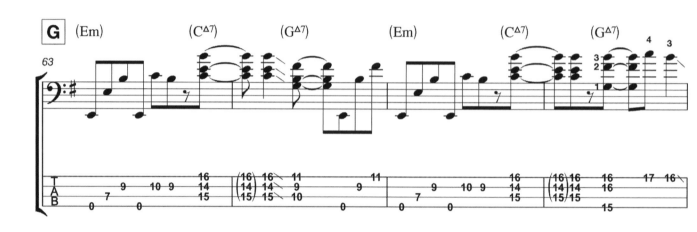

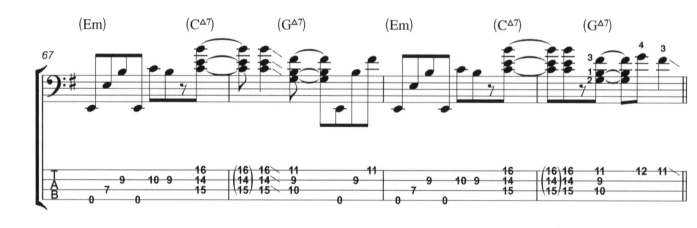

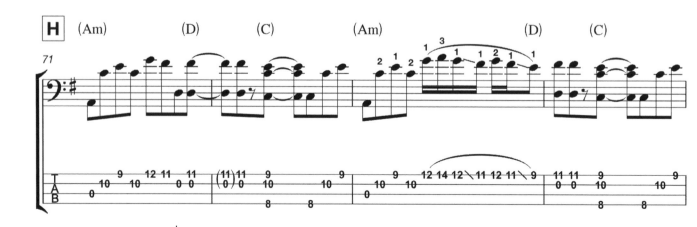

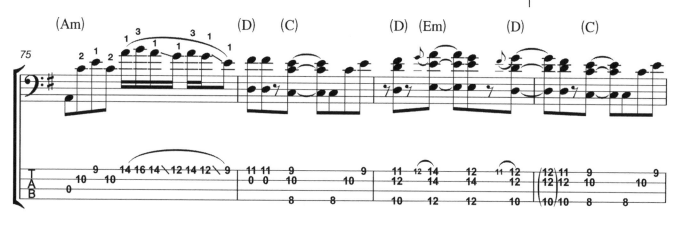

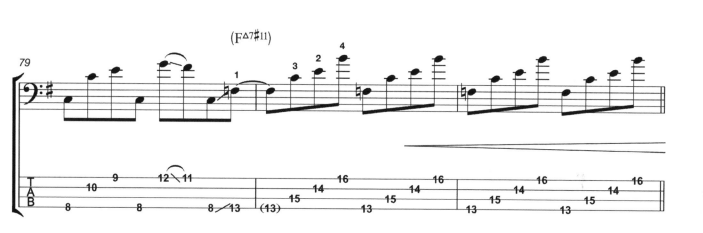

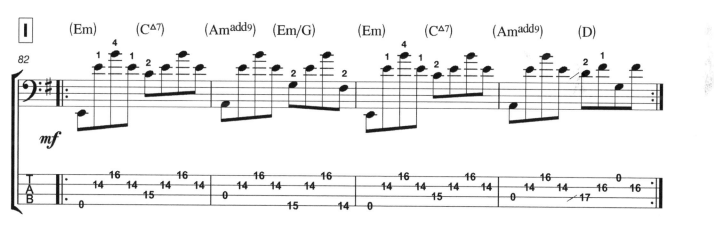

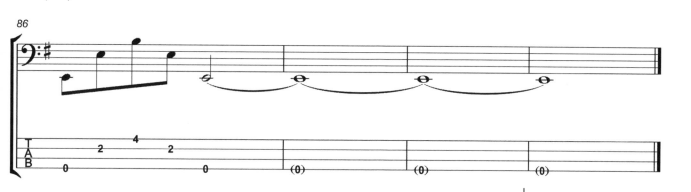

Harmonics Study

This study follows the previous one nicely and is a good piece for working on both the chordal fingerstyle technique and for using natural and artificial harmonics. Harmonics are a fantastic tool for bass players and can be used as decorations, or even as the basis for entire compositions, as Jaco Pastorius famously proved with his harmonics-laden masterpiece 'Portrait of Tracy'.

The A section of this piece is performed using the chordal fingerstyle technique: play the open A's with the thumb of your picking hand and use the first and second fingers to pluck the harmonics on the D and G-strings respectively. Using the chordal fingerstyle technique will allow all of the notes to ring into one another, which is the desired effect here. At the end of the second bar the A moves down to a G, then an F. I recommend fretting the G with the third or fourth finger, then using the first finger for the F - this transition happens quickly so you'll need to practice this slowly to begin with. Once on the F, you can play the harmonic at the third fret of the A-string with the fourth finger and the harmonics at the second fret with the third. Remember that your fingers do not need to continue fretting the harmonics, they will carry on ringing after you lift your finger, unlike fretted notes. You might find that you need to play the second fret harmonics with your fretting finger slightly ahead of the second fret (more towards the third fret) in order for them to ring out at the correct pitch. In the fourth bar of the sequence the low G is fretted with the first finger. The fourth finger is then used for the harmonics at the fifth fret, the third finger for the fourth fret and the second finger for the harmonic at the third fret. This entire four-bar line is played four times.

The part at letter B is the main melody section and consists of fretted melody notes in combination with harmonics. The C^{add9} chord is played with the fourth finger fretting the C on the E-string, the third finger fretting the harmonic on the A-string and the fourth finger fretting the harmonics on the D and G-strings. The C and D melody notes at the end of this bar should then be played with the first and third fingers of the fretting hand. In the second bar I would advise you to fret the double stop tenth with the second finger on the C and the third finger on the top E. This will leave the first finger free to play the harmonics at the seventh fret and the fourth

will be in position to play the F at the tenth fret of the G-string at the beginning of beat four. You'll then need to switch to a new hand position for the F^6 chord that falls on the second half of the fourth beat: fret the F with the second finger and use the first to barre across the seventh fret harmonics on the D and G-strings. This chord is then tied over into the next bar and arpeggiated using the chordal fingerstyle technique. The fourth bar of this section is identical to the fourth bar from the Intro.

The second half of this section begins with the same two bars as before, but the following two are different. In the third bar, the $F^{6/9}$ chord should be fretted as follows: F on the E-string with the second finger, the D on the D-string with the first and the A on the G-string with the third. This will leave the fourth finger available to play the F on the D-string at the end of the bar. The final bar of this sequence uses artificial harmonics. These are played by fretting the notes that are not in brackets, then resting the edge of the picking hand thumb against the string exactly one octave above the fretted note - these 'imaginary' fret positions are the ones shown in the brackets. The string is then plucked behind the thumb with either the first or second fingers of the picking hand - this is shown in the photograph on the next page. For the first chord - $Gsus^4$ - you will be fretting notes at both the fifteenth and seventeenth frets, so your picking hand will need to move from side to side accordingly in order to remain an octave above the fretted notes. The $Gsus^4$ chord resolves to G in the second half of the bar. Artificial harmonics sound very effective as they are well outside of the bass guitar's conventional register. Unfortunately, using them is tricky and they can be difficult to apply quickly.

TIP!

You can also try playing artificial harmonics using the 'Billy Sheehan method'. Billy keeps his picking hand in the standard position for fingerstyle playing and rests the pad of his thumb on the string at the desired point. He then plucks the string with the fingernail of his first finger. The idea here is that the nail is harder and will more closely resemble the sound of a plectrum, which a guitar player would use to play artificial harmonics.

The C section is similar to the Intro, although the first two bars begin with some simple arpeggiated chords before moving to harmonics. The second time through (starting at bar 17), more arpeggiated chords are played in an ascending pattern.

The D and E sections of this piece are repeats of the earlier B and C sections. The only difference is the final four note figure of bar 36, which serves to smooth the transition from the E section into the F section, which is in the key of G minor.

At letter F the piece modulates to G minor and a new part begins. The first two arpeggiated chords are played as a combination of fretted notes and harmonics and should be fingered as follows: for the E♭△7 chord, play the E♭ at the sixth fret of the A-string with the second finger. This will leave the first finger free to fret the harmonics at the fifth fret. Move this fingering up two frets for the F6/9 chord that follows it. The next chord is a wide-spaced voicing of G minor that is decorated with artificial harmonics. Fret the G with the first finger, the D with the second and the high B♭ with the fourth. The top two notes are then played as artificial harmonics whilst the G continues to ring. Remember that your picking hand will need to move from side to side slightly in order for the thumb to be exactly an octave above the fretted notes. The third bar of this sequence reuses the chords from the first bar and the fourth bar is a simple turnaround that will enable you to repeat the part. This line is played four times, with a change to a G major chord - using the same voicing from the A section - in the last bar. This enables a simple modulation back to the original key. The final section of this piece is a repeat of the melody section first heard at letter B.

Of all of the pieces in this book, this is one of the most challenging. There are some difficult fingerings to navigate during the course of this piece and the addition of the artificial harmonics adds a further layer of difficulty! You'll be pleased with yourself once you have this one down - I know I was!

Sound Advice

I performed this piece using my GB Rumour bass. This bass has a 3-band EQ, which is very useful when performing pieces that use a lot of harmonics. When recording, I favoured the bridge pickup slightly and

boosted the mid frequencies - this really helps to bring out the harmonics, particularly the very high pitched ones at the second and third fret positions. If your bass does not have a mid control, try boosting the mid frequencies from your amp instead. A little reverb and/or chorus will sound nice when performing this piece as well.

Playing artificial harmonics

Recommended Listening

1. 'Portrait of Tracy' - Jaco Pastorius

2. 'Birdland' - Weather Report (Jaco Pastorius on bass)

3. 'Port of Entry' - Weather Report (Jaco Pastorius on bass)

4. 'I, Resolute' - Zander Zon

5. 'Looking Glass' - Zander Zon

6. 'Tribal Chant' - Zander Zon

7. 'I Left America' - Michael Manring

8. 'NV43345' - Talas (Billy Sheehan on bass)

9. 'Selene' - Michael Manring

10. 'Tree' - Randy Coven

Harmonics Study

Written by Stuart Clayton

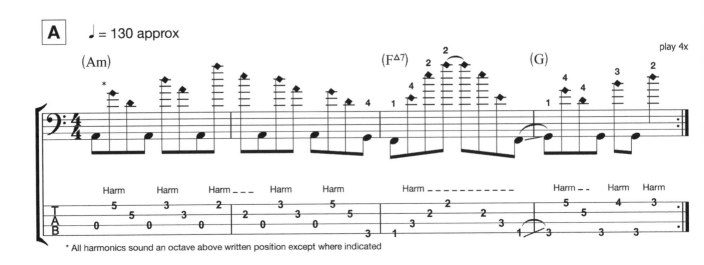

* All harmonics sound an octave above written position except where indicated

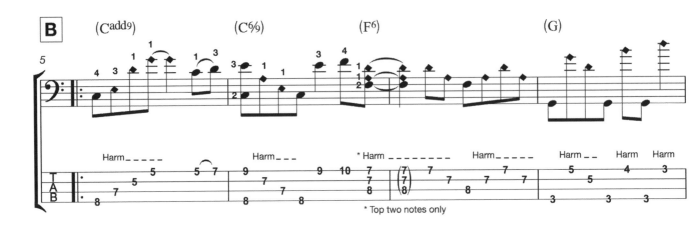

* Top two notes only

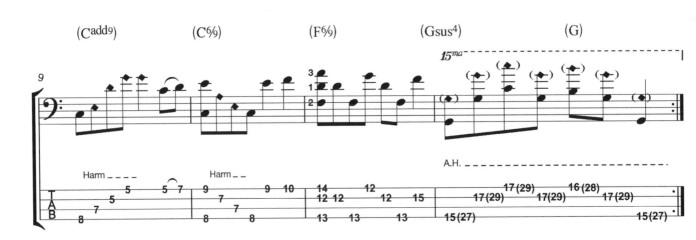

ADVANCED STUDIES FOR BASS GUITAR

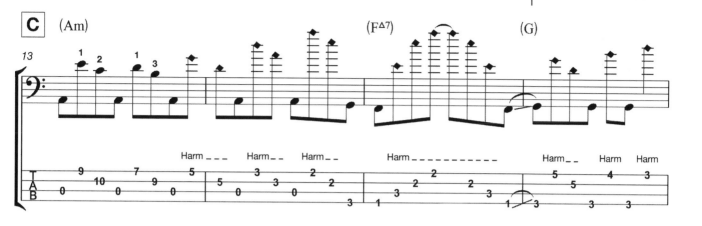

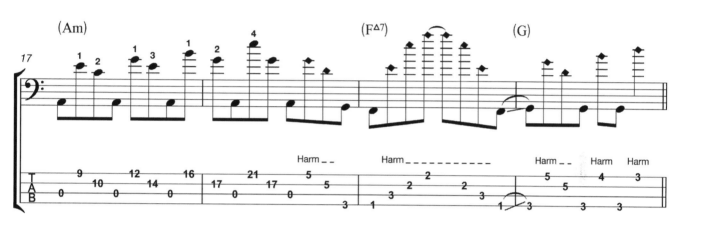

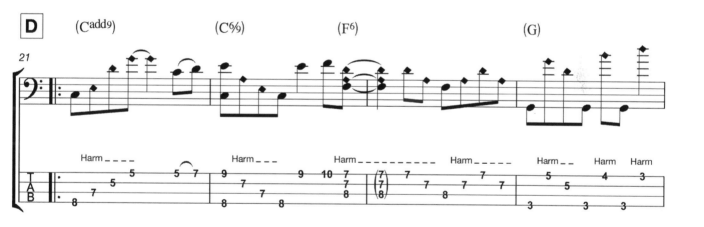

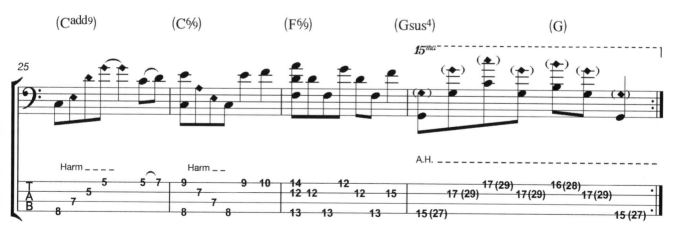

ADVANCED STUDIES FOR BASS GUITAR

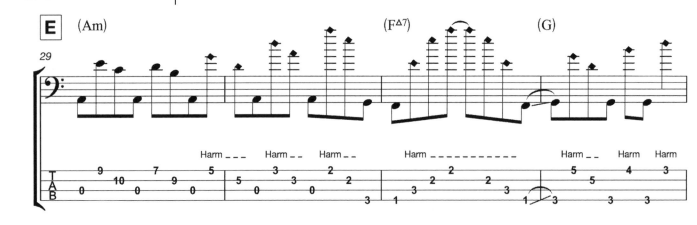

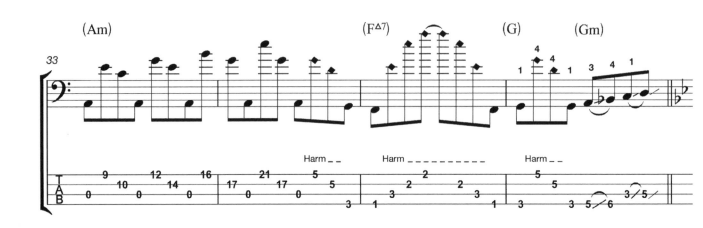

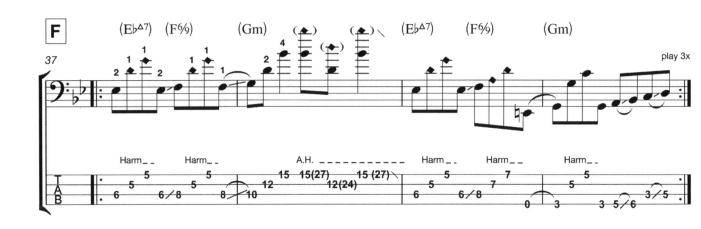

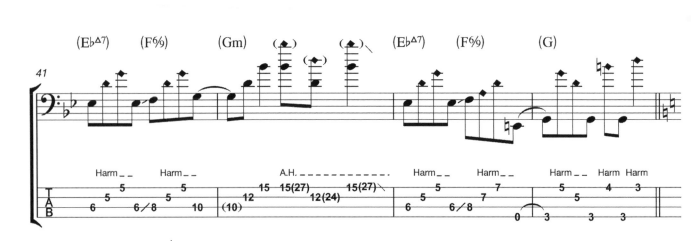

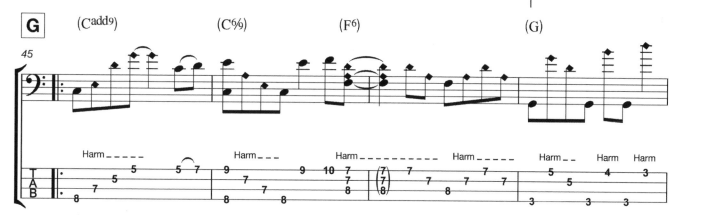

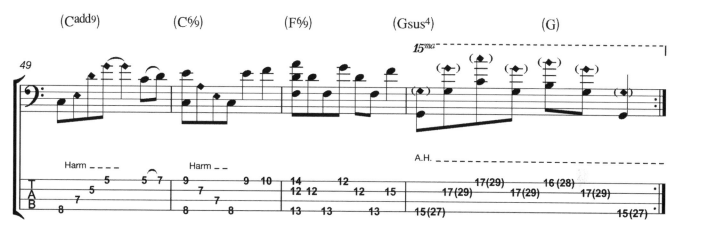

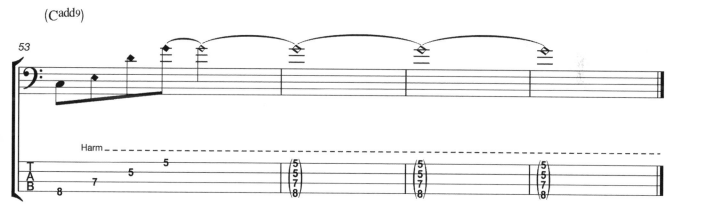

Plectrum Study No. 1

This piece is a plectrum study written in the style of funk/rock groups such as Extreme, The Electric Boys and Faith No More. As is typical with the genre, the bass plays quite an active role here, doubling most of the tricky guitar lines and playing complex, syncopated but supportive parts that really bring the piece to life.

The A section features a simple guitar line that outlines an E^7 tonality. Beneath this, the bass sustains a low E before doubling the figures in the second and fourth bars. The first of these (bar 2), reinforces the dominant quality of the chord by sliding up the neck to play the seventh (D) and major third (G$\sharp$) of the chord. These notes are a tritone apart, which gives them a very distinctive sound - in fact, the third and seventh are the two most colourful notes in a dominant chord and are often used in this way, particularly in funk music. The line in bar 4 is a simple phrase that makes use of the blues scale. The blues scale is another popular choice in funk (and rock) music and the flattened fifth and minor third (against a major chord backing) sound very distinctive here. This four bar section is then repeated. For the next four bars, the guitar becomes more active, playing an $E^{7\sharp 9}$ chord whilst the bass plays a simple figure on the first beat of the bar.

At letter B the first riff section begins. This part is played in unison with the guitar and is semiquaver-based. You will need to be very comfortable playing busy semiquaver lines with a pick in order to execute this successfully: remember that the correct placement of down and upstrokes is hugely important to playing lines such as this to a high standard, so be sure to follow the picking guides written between the staves.

The phrase that opens each bar of the riff contains a pull-off from the first note to the second - E to D. The E should be played with a downstroke and your picking hand should then perform a 'silent upstroke' whilst the pull-off is played by the fretting hand. This will enable you to play another downstroke on the third note of the beat - the B on the E-string. This note in turn is followed by an upstroke, which plays the open E. Following this, you will need to play a silent downstroke on beat two in order to play the ghost note with an upstroke. This will mean that you can begin the third beat on a downstroke, which is usually the strongest stroke for most pick players. Playing semiquaver lines with a

pick often requires you to play a continuous semiquaver down-up pattern with the picking hand. Some of these strokes will be silent and will be used simply to keep you in time and enable you to start each beat with a downstroke. This is how most rhythm guitar players will approach semiquaver rhythms when playing grooves such as this.

> **TIP!**
>
> *If you need additional help with playing semiquaver-based lines with a pick, the topic is covered in detail in* Plectrum Technique for Bass Guitar, *also available from Bassline Publishing.*

The fill in the fourth bar of this riff (bar 12) is a little more complex: after the initial pull-off phrase, there is a semiquaver rest followed by a fast pull-off figure that is played with one picked upstroke. An upstroke has been specified here as the phrase begins on the second semiquaver of the beat, one which would typically be played with an upstroke. In reality, it doesn't matter a great deal if you use a downstroke here, as there is plenty of time to adjust your picking hand before the next pick stroke. The four notes on the third beat are played followed a strict down-up pattern and the final group of three notes is played with two downstrokes as a hammer-on is played on the second semiquaver. This entire four bar riff is then repeated, but with a different ending the second time. The final bar is the only one that is different and has a descending blues scale riff played as an offset group of four semiquavers. Extreme used a similar idea to this during the instrumental section of their hit song 'Get the Funk Out'. It's important that you follow the picking guides here - in particular watch out for the second group of four notes, which starts on the second semiquaver of the second beat and therefore should be played starting with an upstroke.

At letter C a new section begins featuring another energetic bassline. This time the line is more root-based however, so there is less awkward string crossing to contend with. Watch out for the phrase at the end of the second bar (bar 16) - on the final beat you will play a downstroke C on the A-string followed by an upstroke F$\sharp$ on the E-string. This happens quite quickly, but if you keep the wrist of your picking hand as relaxed as possible you shouldn't find this bit of string crossing too difficult. The final bar of this riff (bar 18) is played in unison with the guitar. Be sure to play the hammer-ons as written and be aware that they will have a bearing on the picking pattern that should be used.

A busier line begins at letter D, which features a new chord sequence with a change in every bar. This line is based on the quaver-two semiquavers pattern, but features some tied rhythms as well that add a significant degree of syncopation to the part. In particular, watch out for the tie between the second and third beats of bar 19 - this will require you to play two upstrokes in a row, with a silent downstroke being played through the tied note. The same thing happens in the following bar as well, which also features a lot of string crossing - remember to keep the wrist of your picking hand relaxed at all times. This section is followed by the E section - the main theme - which is a straight repeat of the earlier B section.

After a three-bar guitar break, the bass re-enters in bar 32 with a long descending blues scale fill. This is played as continuous semiquavers, so the picking pattern is relatively simple here. The only thing to watch out for is the final beat: the A and G are played with a down and upstroke respectively, then a silent downstroke is played before the final E is played with an upstroke. This E falls on the final semiquaver of the beat and is an important part of the next riff.

At letter F a long unison section begins - this was inspired by the Extreme track 'Cupid's Dead' which has a lengthy instrumental unison section in place of a guitar solo. The first riff opens with a syncopated phrase that continues from the low E at the end of the previous bar. After continuing the tie into the first semiquaver of the beat, the remainder of beat one is played as semiquavers using a logical up-down-up sequence. The remainder of the bar is played with continuous down-up strokes with the exception of the hammer-on on beat two. There's quite a lot of string crossing to contend with here as well, so you should practice this line very slowly to begin with, at all times ensuring that you are following the recommended pick strokes. This riff ends in bar 38 with a long descending phrase with a pull-off figure that is similar to the one played during the B and E sections.

At bar 39 a new line begins, still played in unison with the guitar. Again, this is a continuous semiquaver riff, but features a lot of hammer-ons and some tied notes. This syncopates the line quite heavily, meaning that upstrokes are played more than downstrokes. Although this will be awkward initially, you should find that following the picking guide will ensure that your hand maintains the correct picking sequence. The same advice holds true for the final riff in this section, which begins in bar 51.

This is a very complex study and will present a real challenge to your plectrum playing. Remember that although the phrases are complex, they are all based on the continuous down-up semiquaver picking pattern. You should find that working on this piece helps you to conquer the use of silent down and upstrokes which are essential to playing lines such as this to a high standard.

Sound Advice

I recorded this piece using a Fender Jazz American Standard bass and a Dunlop Tortex .73mm pick. The bass was recorded direct into Logic, where it was compressed and EQ'd as needed.

Recommended Listening

1. 'Get the Funk Out' - Extreme
2. 'Cupid's Dead' - Extreme
3. 'Decadence Dance' - Extreme
4. 'Rest in Peace' - Extreme (all with Pat Badger on bass)
5. 'Land of Sunshine' - Faith No More (Billy Gould on bass)
6. 'Captain of My Soul' - The Electric Boys
7. 'Rags to Riches' - The Electric Boys
8. 'Straight No Chaser' - The Electric Boys
9. My Heart's Not for Sale - The Electric Boys
10. 'The House is Rockin' - The Electric Boys (all with Andy Christell on bass)

Plectrum Study No. 1

Written by Stuart Clayton

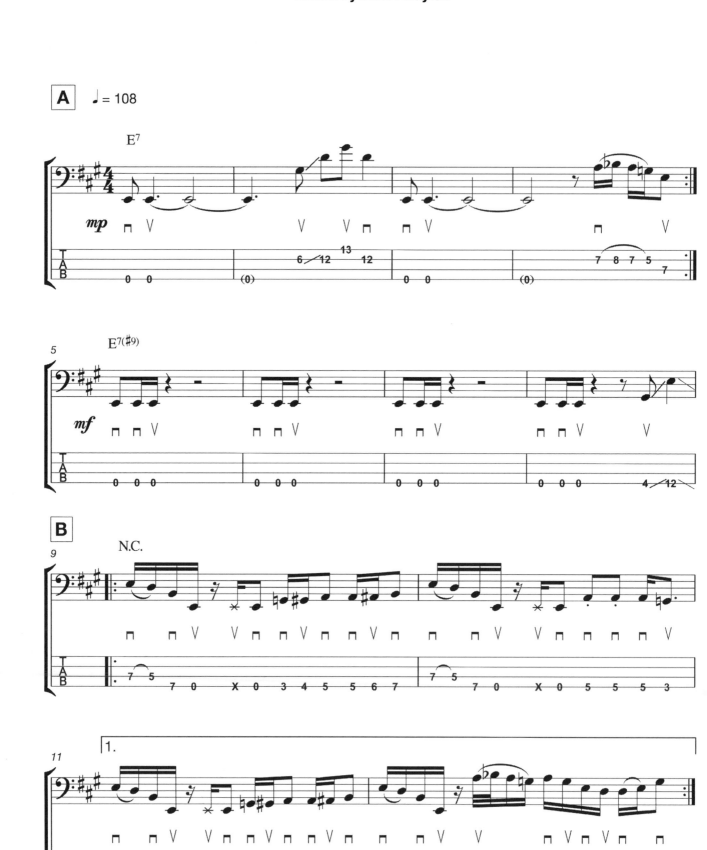

ADVANCED STUDIES FOR BASS GUITAR

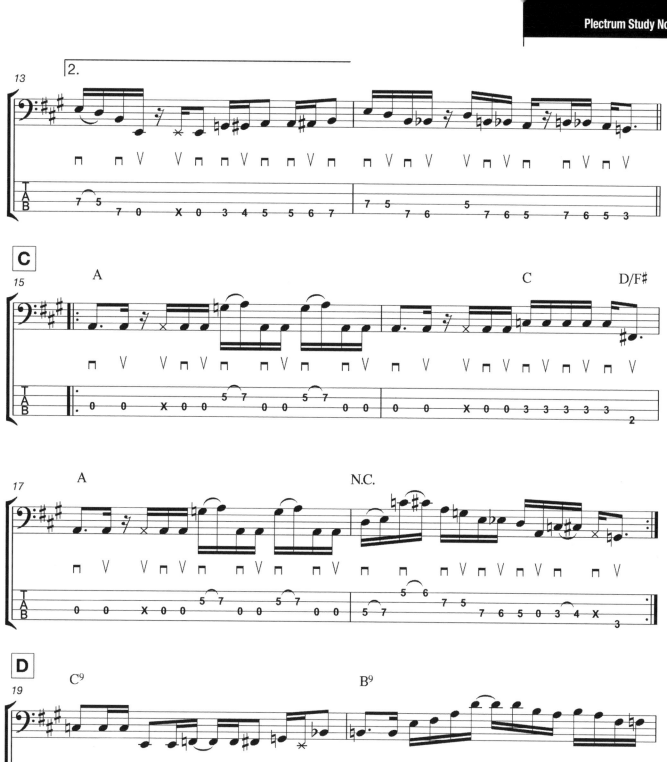

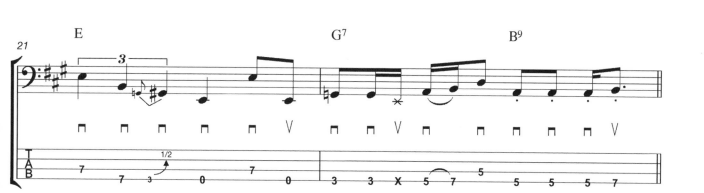

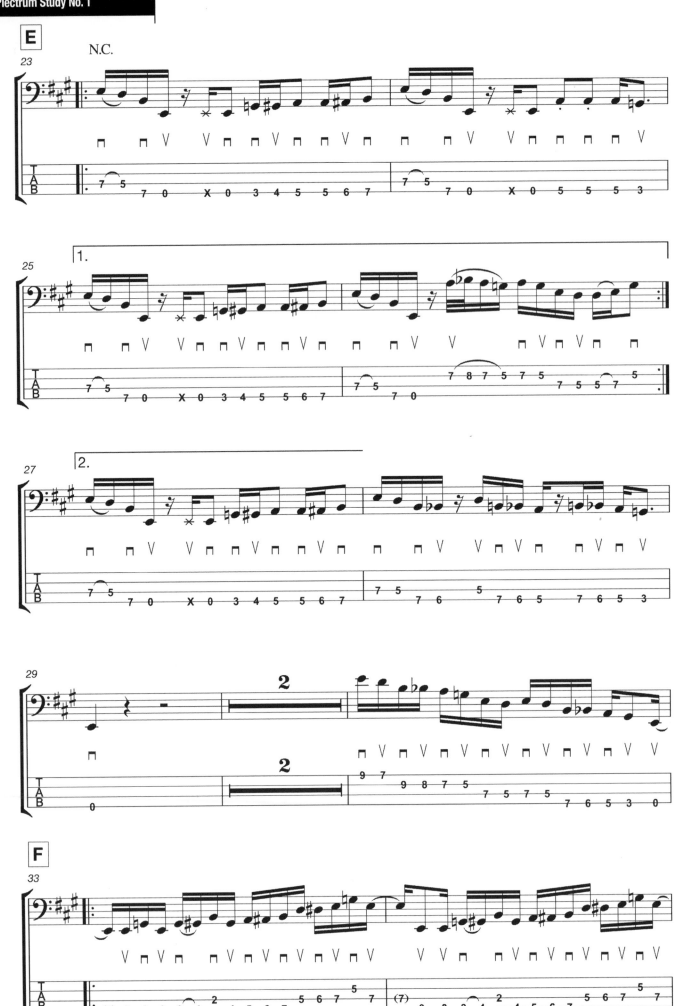

ADVANCED STUDIES FOR BASS GUITAR

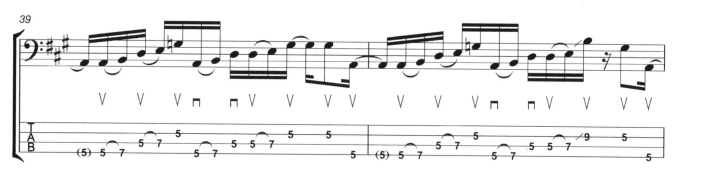

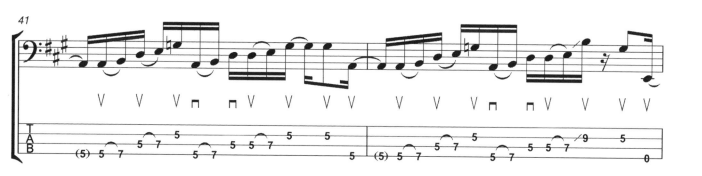

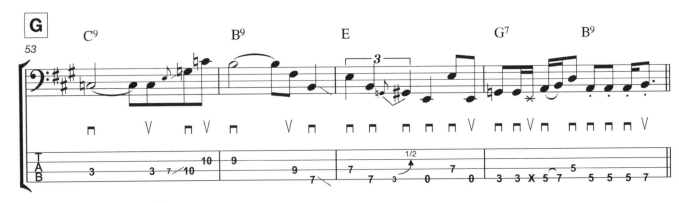

Plectrum Study No. 2

This second plectrum study is something that I wrote whilst learning to utilise the plectrum for semiquaver-based funk grooves. Playing funk with a pick is not something that many bass players typically do, although legendary players such as Carol Kaye, Anthony Jackson and Bobby Vega have all shown that the two can go together extremely well.

It's important that you follow the picking guides written between the staves when learning this piece. The suggested picking pattern follows a semiquaver-based continuous down-up rhythm which allows complex funk parts to be played cleanly with the plectrum. If you do not follow this sequence, there is a danger of playing upbeats with downstrokes, which will not only feel quite uncomfortable, but which will also lead to problems playing the line accurately.

The A section of this composition uses double stop chords combined with ghost notes to fill out the rhythm. As suggested by the picking guides, you should play the chord at the end of the first beat of the first bar with an upstroke - this will ensure that you start the second beat with a downstroke. The triplet phrase on the third beat is played using hammer-ons and pull-offs, with the note on the A-string at the end of the beat played with an upstroke of the plectrum. The hammer-on at the beginning of the fourth beat is played with a downstroke. The following note can also be played with a downstroke, although an upstroke would also be acceptable here. The next bar in the sequence is played in exactly the same way, but a tone lower. In the third bar, the same picking pattern is used again for the first two beats of the bar. The open A should then be allowed to ring whilst you play the ascending phrase on the D-string. This line moves chromatically upwards to the major third of the chord (C#), which outlines the harmony nicely. The fourth and final bar of the sequence uses a simple semiquaver rhythm to play two further chords, C^5 and D^5. Make sure that the ghost notes are played as such here - these are rhythmic devices, intended to keep the groove moving along.

At letter B a complex semiquaver funk bassline is introduced. When playing this line, it's vital that your picking hand moves in the continuous semiquaver down-up motion described earlier. When playing the first beat,

you will play the B with a downstroke, then play the C# as a hammer-on. Whilst your fretting hand is hammering on, the picking hand will play a 'silent upstroke', ready to hit the ghost note with a downbeat. This ghost note is followed by an E, played with an upstroke on the A-string. As you will discover, it can be quite challenging to play a downstroke on one string and the upstroke on another. If you are struggling with this, I would recommend that you practice this first phrase in isolation at a slower tempo for a while before tackling the rest of the line. The second beat begins with a rest, which should be 'played' with a silent downstroke from the picking hand, meaning the remainder of the notes on this beat will fall into place easily. The phrase on the third beat also requires a silent downstroke: play the D on the G-string twice (down, up), then follow it with a pull-off to the C# on the fret below. Whilst this pull-off is performed, the picking hand should play a silent downstroke, enabling the second C# to be played with an upstroke. This will put you comfortably onto a downstroke for the beginning of the fourth beat. This bar is then repeated twice more. The final bar of the sequence uses a turnaround figure that is played using the same techniques already described. As stated above, the key to getting this section to sound good is to maintain the continuous semiquaver picking pattern throughout the bar (some pick strokes will be silent). This will really help with the groove, as will the correct placement of the hammer-ons and pull-offs. This section is then played for a second time, the only difference being the use of four E's at the beginning of bar 8. This section is followed by a repeat of the chordal riff first heard at the beginning of the piece.

TIP!

For further help with semiquaver-based alternate picking technique, check out Plectrum Technique for Bass Guitar, *also available from Bassline Publishing.*

At letter D a new section begins, one that serves as a bridge between the C section and E section. It begins with an abrupt modulation (key change) to E♭ major. If you have successfully worked through the previous two sections, this part should not present too much of a problem to you, but watch out for

ADVANCED STUDIES FOR BASS GUITAR

the phrase on the third beat of the bar: after ascending on the D-string, the line reaches G - the third of the chord - at the beginning of the third beat, then immediately drops an octave to the low G on the E-string. This skip from the D-string down to the E-string within two semiquavers requires good control over your picking hand, so work on this bar slowly and in isolation to begin with. The remaining bars of this section are a little simpler, with the chords moving up sequentially from B♭, to C, to D, to D/E, at which point the piece modulates back to the original key for the E section.

At letter E a new line begins, based around an A⁷ chord. The beginning of each bar has a chord played as an open A-string, with a double stop containing the major third and flattened seventh played in the upper register. You should slide up into this double stop. Note that a second A falls on the final semiquaver subdivision of this beat - this should be played with an upstroke, putting you onto a downstroke for the second beat. The third and fourth beats are different in each of the next three bars, although each fill outlines the A⁷ chord in some way. All of these parts are played using the picking techniques already described in these notes. Throughout this section, you should again be keeping a continuous semiquaver picking rhythm happening with your picking hand. The piece ends with a final reading of the main chordal theme.

Good luck with this one. This is a difficult piece to get together, mostly because of the semiquaver-picking patterns and string-crossing that is required. Groove is extremely important when playing these lines, but if you're playing them right, you'll find that they feel great.

Sound Advice

I performed this piece using my 1972 Fender Jazz bass, string with very dead roundwound strings. I played the line using a Dunlop Tortex 0.73mm plectrum which is very flexible - I find that thin, flexible picks work really well for percussive funk playing as heard here.

This track was performed on a 1972 Fender Jazz Bass

Recommended Listening

1. 'For the Love of Money' - The O'Jays (Anthony Jackson on bass)

2. 'Games People Play' - Mel Torme (Carol Kaye on bass)

3. 'Hikky Burr' - Qunicy Jones and Bill Cosby (Carol Kaye on bass)

4. 'Boogaloo' - Carol Kaye

5. 'Bass Catch' - Carol Kaye

6. 'Burning Spear' - Carol Kaye

7. 'Xs' - Bobby Vega

8. 'Buttermilk' - Bobby Vega

9. 'Apocolyptic' - Bobby Vega and Chris Rossbach (Bobby Vega on bass)

10. 'Mothra' - Bobby Vega and Chris Rossbach (Bobby Vega on bass)

Plectrum Study No. 2

Written by Stuart Clayton

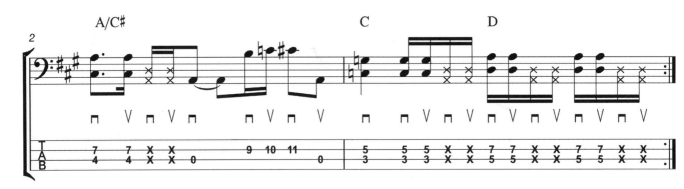

ADVANCED STUDIES FOR BASS GUITAR

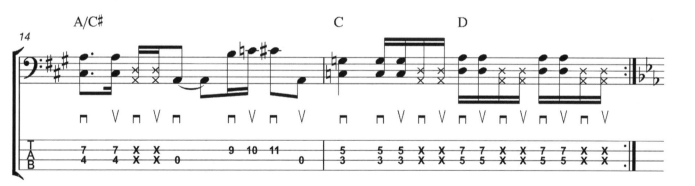

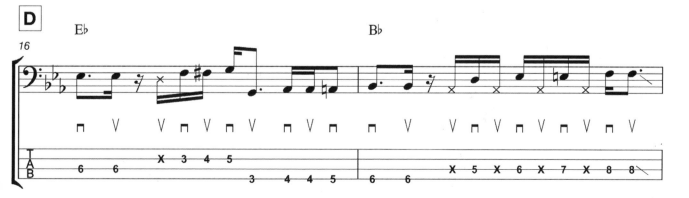

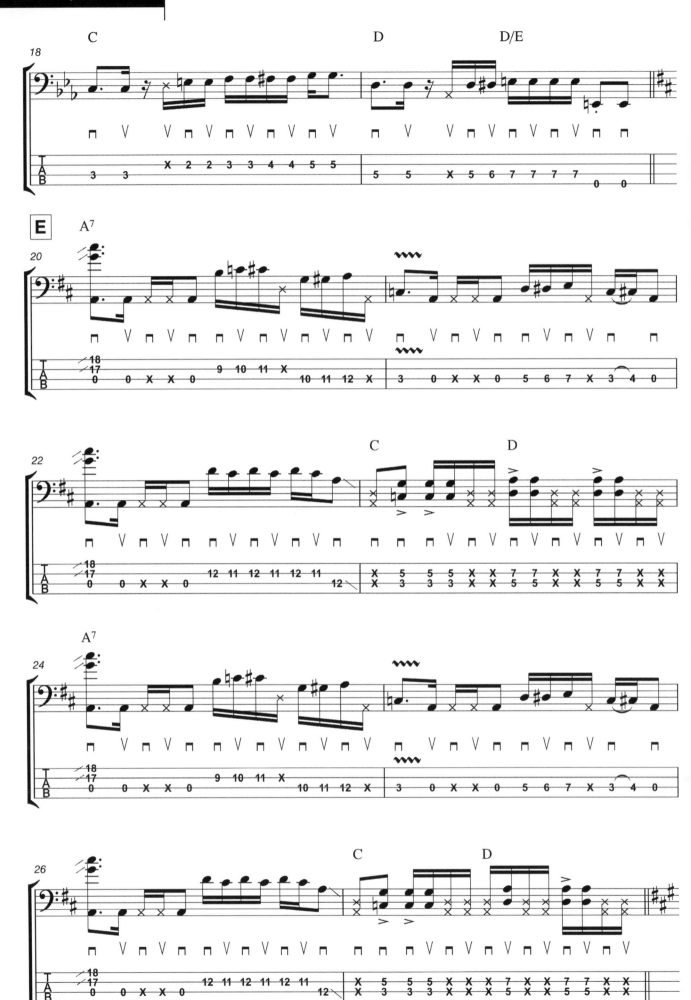

ADVANCED STUDIES FOR BASS GUITAR

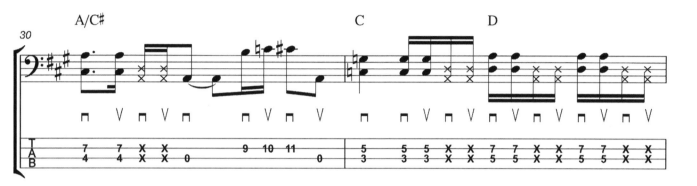

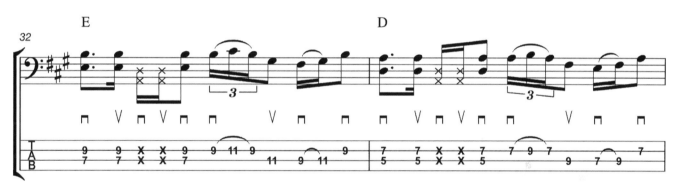

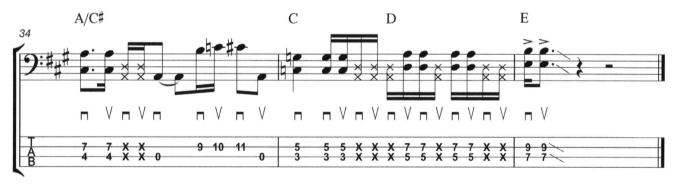

Slap Bass Study No. 1

This slap bass study - the first of two in this book - is written in the style of legendary bassist Marcus Miller. The main challenge with this piece is using the slap technique at a slower tempo, with a strong focus on the groove. This is something that Marcus is renowned for. It's also a great piece for working on your double popping technique - using both the first and second fingers of the picking hand to pop the strings.

The A section of this piece begins with an upper register voicing of an Am^7 chord which should be plucked with the thumb and the first two fingers on the A, D and G-strings respectively. This chord is followed by a slide from the octave A down to the open A-string. A simple rhythmic figure using ghost notes completes the first bar. In the second bar of the riff a descending minor pentatonic lick is played using a series of hammer-ons. When slapping the C at the end of the second beat, bend it upwards in pitch a little: it's marked as a ¼ tone bend, so should only be bent slightly. A ½ tone bend would be a semitone, C - C♯, which would then imply a major sound, so be sure not to bend the note this far. This bar then ends in the same way as the previous one. In the fourth bar a longer descending lick is played. This time, the line begins in the previous bar, with a slide up into the 'blue note', E♭. When playing this lick you will likely find that it is quite tough to slap and pop on the same string in quick succession. This is a technique that Marcus employs frequently however and is great for playing melodic lines such as this one. You should practice this slowly and out of tempo to begin with. This part is played slightly differently the second time through, with the climax of the line building up to the introduction of the melody line in the next section. When playing this part - which will reoccur several times throughout - remember to focus on your timing: you should be playing directly on the beat - or if anything very slightly behind - rather than pushing it. A tight, solid groove is everything here.

At letter B the bass plays the melody line, interspersed with some slapped root notes. A synth bass takes care of the majority of the low end here, leaving the bass guitar free to play melodically - again, this is a common fixture in Marcus's compositions. Try to keep the slapped low A's in this section staccato, as written. You'll see that the simple melody remains much the same throughout this part, while the bass notes below it change, altering the meaning of the notes played. The final bar of this section features a busier line that outlines an E^7 chord. Some double popped demisemiquaver ghost notes are used here. To play this phrase, slap the low E, then immediately pop the D and G-string ghost notes with the first and second fingers in quick succession. These pops will be immediately followed by a ghost note thumb slap on the E-string, then another pop on the G-string. This kind of figure is also something Marcus uses often, and you can hear it on songs such as 'Rio' (recorded with Lee Ritenour) and 'Run for Cover', which is one of Marcus's best-known compositions. This part leads directly into letter C, which is a repeat of the main theme from letter A. Watch out for the alternative fill that is played at the end of this section (bar 22) - this legato phrase is played by popping the string just once, then performing the remainder of the notes with hammer-ons and pull-offs. This lick will be used more extensively in the next part of the piece.

At letter D a new part begins, again with the bass playing the main melody. Tenths (compound major and minor thirds) are used extensively here to supply the harmony. This part essentially consists of a long melody note in each bar, with a simple bass rhythm played beneath. The melodic lick from the end of the previous section is used at the end of each bar to set up the next chord change. When playing this line, it is recommended that you fret the E on the G-string with your third finger. This will enable you to play the F with your fourth, while your first can fret the D at the seventh fret for the pull-off. Throughout this part of the piece you should let all of the notes ring as much as you possibly can in order to fully reflect the sound of the chord.

TIP!

Marcus Miller is one of the most melodic slap players out there and often uses the technique to play very lyrical phrases, often with rather vocal-like phrasing. When working on this section of the piece you might find it useful to study (and even transcribe) some of his melodic lines on tracks such as 'Power', 'Blast' and 'Detroit'.

At letter E is a bass solo. In typical Marcus Miller style, this part consists of simple pentatonic lines combined with more complex rhythmic figures. The solo opens with the double popped figure that was used earlier at the end of the B section, although this time it begins from the open A-string. This is followed by an A minor pentatonic lick. As before, the tricky part of this line is slapping and popping on the same string: after playing the D to E hammer-on at the beginning of beat two, a G is popped at the fifth fret of the D-string, then immediately slapped with the thumb and followed with a hammer-on to the A. After a popped ghost note on the G-string, the A slides up to a C and on the final beat of the bar the chord that opened the piece is played as an arpeggio using a syncopated rhythm. This one-bar lick is then repeated twice more. In the fourth bar of the solo the syncopated arpeggio figure is played three times in total, ending this section of the solo.

The second half of the solo has more focus on rhythm and double pops are again used at the beginning of each bar. However, with the exception of the first bar, the slapped first note falls on the final semiquaver of the bar before, meaning that there is a slight delay between the slapped note and the popped notes. This rhythmic displacement adds an extra layer of syncopation to the solo which works well. Aside from open A's, the only pitched notes in this section are chord tones which are popped on the G-string: these are all popped quite aggressively and followed with quick downward glissandos (slides). The solo ends with the bluesy minor pentatonic lick from the main section. When learning this solo - which is simple by Marcus Miller's standards - be sure to check out tracks such as 'Rio' and others from the list opposite.

The final section of this study (section F) is a repeat of the main theme, first heard back at letter A. The piece then ends with the opening Am^7 chord.

This piece is very challenging, but you will hopefully find working through it very enjoyable. You can afford to be quite aggressive in your slapping in most parts of this study (the exception is letter D, which should be played a little more delicately) and as I have stated already several times, remember that the groove is the most important thing here. The most common

mistake made when playing pieces of this nature is rushing, so concentrate hard on your time-keeping at all times.

Sound Advice

This track was performed on a bass which has been retrofitted with Sims Super Quad pickups. These pickups can be figured as single coils, split coils or as humbuckers. I used single coils to emulate the active Fender Jazz sound as used by Marcus Miller. Any Fender Jazz bass will get you close to the required tone. I recommend favouring the neck pickup slightly. Some compression will also help tighten up the sound.

This piece was recorded using an old bass retrofitted with Sims Super Quad pickups

Recommended Listening

1. 'Power' - Marcus Miller

2. 'Nikki's Groove' - Marcus Miller

3. 'Run for Cover' - David Sanborn (Marcus Miller on bass)

4. 'Bruce Lee' - Marcus Miller

5. 'Rio' - Lee Ritenour (Marcus Miller on bass)

6. 'Frankenstein' - Marcus Miller

7. 'Blast' - Marcus Miller

8. 'Scoop' - Marcus Miller

9. 'Detroit' - Marcus Miller

10. 'Cee-Tee-Eye' - Marcus Miller

Slap Bass Study No. 1

Written by Stuart Clayton

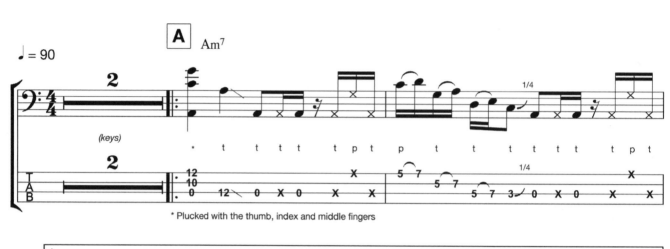

* Plucked with the thumb, index and middle fingers

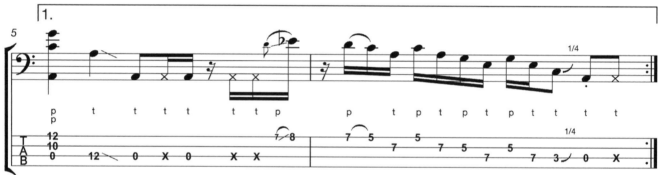

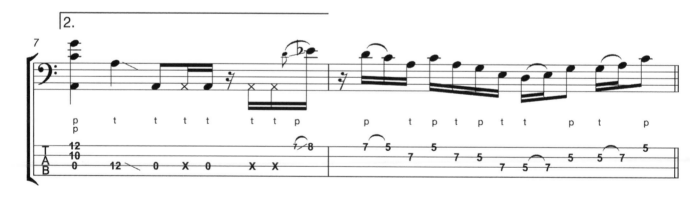

ADVANCED STUDIES FOR BASS GUITAR

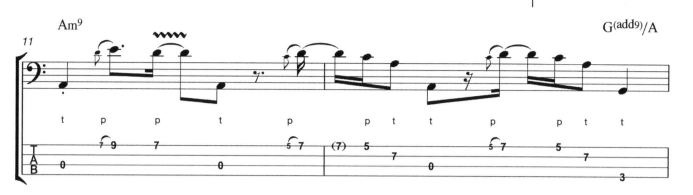

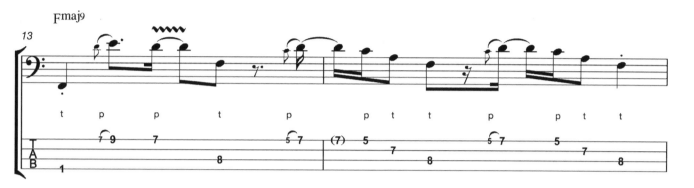

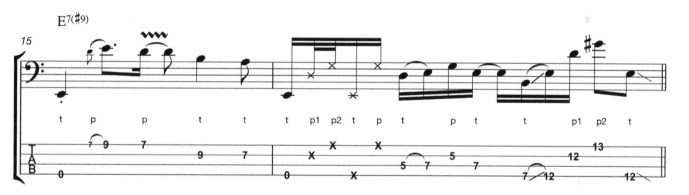

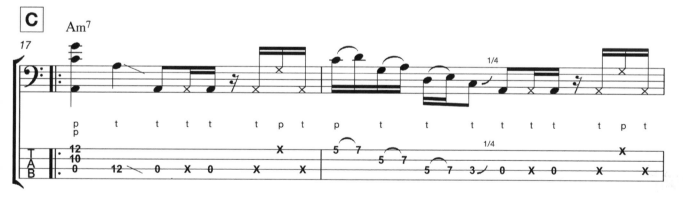

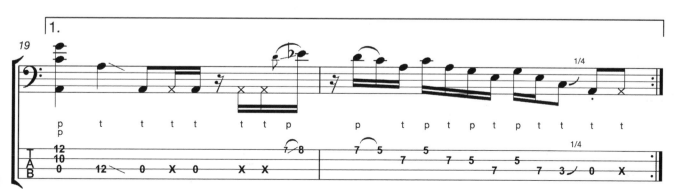

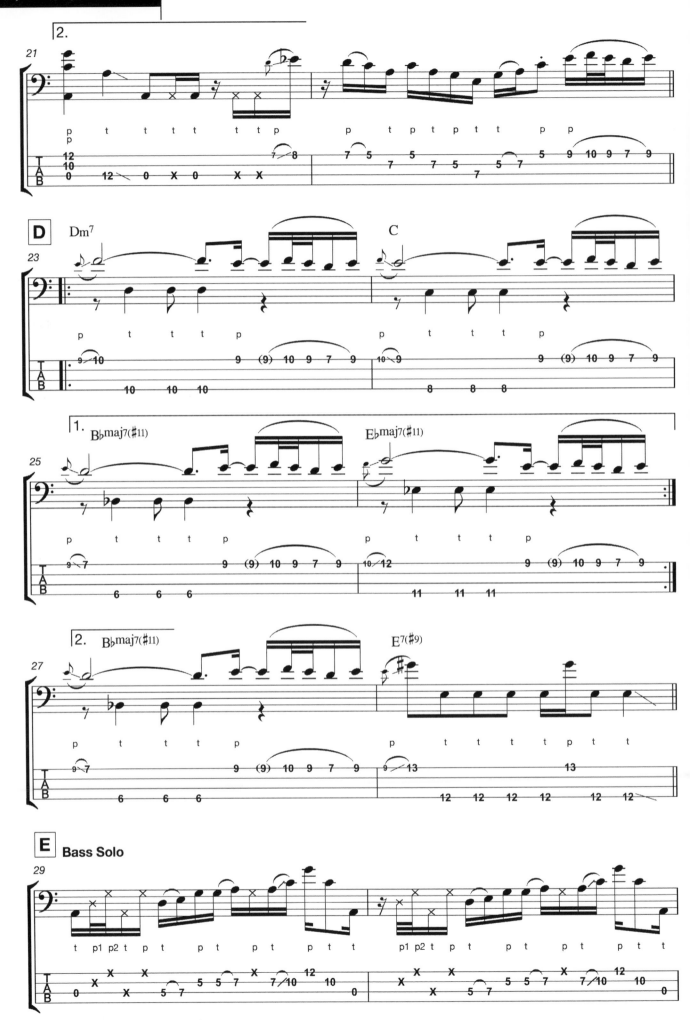

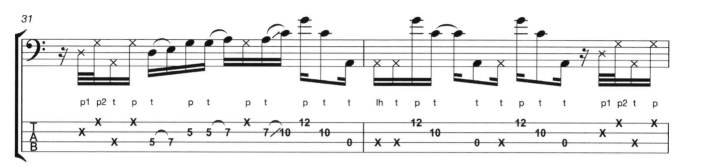

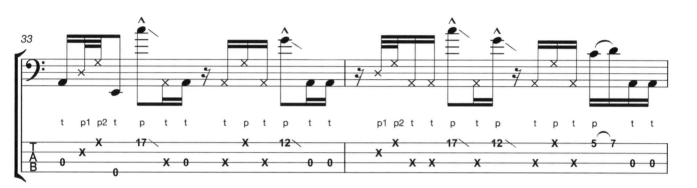

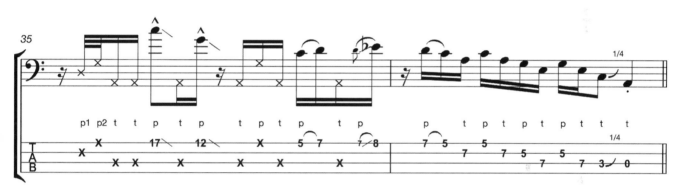

F Am⁷

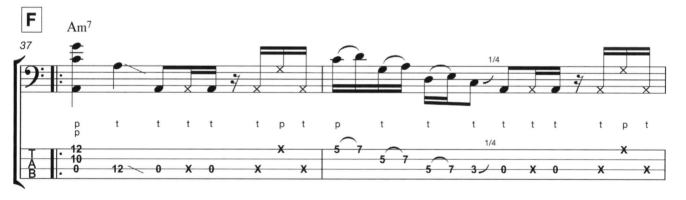

Slap Bass Study No. 2

This second slap bass study moves at a quicker tempo than the previous one and features a much busier style of slap playing, one that has been used by bassists such as Stuart Hamm and Mark King, amongst others. This piece specifically focuses on triplet popping, fretting hand slapping and strumming techniques.

Section A features a riff that utilises both triplet popping and strumming, both of which can be tough to execute cleanly at this tempo. To play the figure at the beginning of the first bar, slap the low E with the thumb and then play a quick triplet using the thumb, a first finger pop and a second finger pop. These notes are played as a semiquaver triplet, so will go by quickly and will need to sound as relaxed and fluid as possible. The second pop is immediately followed with a ghost note slap on the E-string, then a strummed E^5 chord at the second fret. This is tied into the third beat - giving your picking hand a moment of respite - before the descending E minor pentatonic lick is played using conventional slap technique. This riff is then repeated twice more, each time substituting the E^5 chord for C^5, then D^5. The phrase ends with a turnaround figure that incorporates some fretting hand slaps. These are played by allowing the fingers of the fretting hand to slap against the strings, creating a dead note. The technique is similar to how you would use your fingers to lightly mute the strings, but is applied with more force. Fretting hand slaps are great for filling in the gaps in slap grooves and add a nice percussive element to the line.

At letter B a busy semiquaver-based slap groove begins. The triplet figure used in the previous riff is used again here but is this time used as the starting point for a complex slap groove that again uses fretting hand slaps to fill in the gaps in the rhythm. The trick to mastering this part is becoming comfortable with slapping notes on the A-string, and allowing the fretting hand to perform ghost note slaps in between. I recommend that you fret the D and C♯ notes with the first finger of the fretting hand - this will leave the other three fingers free for the ghost note slaps in between. Many of these fretting hand slaps are notated on the E-string, since this is typically the string that you will strike when performing them, but don't worry if you play them on the A-string - the important thing is that the note is a ghost note since it is only

there in a rhythmic capacity. The fourth bar of this riff (bar 11) features more semiquaver triplet figures - these are performed in the same way as before, although this time there are three in a row. At bar 12 the line begins again and this time the fourth bar of the sequence is marked by a strummed chordal part. To strum chords on the bass, flick downwards with the fingers of the picking hand, striking the strings with your nails for the maximum attack - this is shown in the photograph on the opposite page. You can then strum upwards, catching the strings with the tips of the fingers. You'll need to be comfortable strumming down and up in order to be able to play this riff accurately. When playing the chords that only use the A and D-strings be sure to mute the G-string with the fretting hand in order to prevent any unwanted notes ringing out. After the B section bassline has been played again, this strumming riff is used again and expanded upon in bars 16 and 17.

> **TIP!**
>
> *For further help with both strumming and double popping techniques, check out* Ultimate Slap Bass, *also available from Bassline Publishing.*

At letter C a new line begins, again using strummed chords. The first of these chords is a tenth chord for D major, using the open D-string. The second is a similar voicing for an A major chord, but with the fifth - E - added at the top of the chord. Both chords are strummed using the technique described above. You should aim to accurately play the rest that separates the two chords as it is important to the overall feel. After you have strummed the A major chord, leave it fretted so that you can play the simple slap and pop figure that completes the bar. This bar is used four times during this section, each time followed by a different slap lick. In the second bar of this section a simple descending phrase (G - F♯ - E and D) is played. Each note is followed by a semiquaver triplet, played with the double popping technique that was described earlier. In the fourth bar of the section (bar 21) an open string popping line is played. This line is essentially a three-note figure played as a slapped note followed by a hammer-on on the same string, which in turn is followed by a popped open string. Although this is a three-note figure, it is played using straight semiquavers, meaning that each time it begins on different part of the beat. Ignoring the first note of each group of three, you can see that melodically, this part is a simple G major pentatonic-based line. The final bar of this section (bar 23) uses a similar idea, this time moving chromatically downwards from the D in order to begin the next section on a C.

Letter D is the final new section of the piece and is based around a C^7 chord - you'll see that this section features a key change to F major to reflect this (C^7 is the V chord in F major). The line begins with a triplet pop figure on a common voicing of a C^7 chord: root (C), third (E) and flattened seventh (B♭). After the ghost notes that begin the third beat, this voicing is switched to another common way of playing the same chord, higher up on the neck. This time the E is played at the top of the voicing, above the B♭ rather than the other way around. The following bar is a bluesy slap riff that features a tricky legato figure on the third and fourth beat. When playing this, fret the F with the fourth finger, slide up to the G♭ and back again, before pulling off to sound the E♭, which should be fretted by the first finger at the sixth fret. The C is then performed with a fretting hand hammer-on. This way of playing the riff uses condensed fingering, which is to use four fingers in the space of three frets. You can also use the finger-per-fret method for this line, but I personally find that it sounds best using condensed fingering. In the fourth bar of this section, the slap part from the second bar is re-used, but is this time followed by a strummed C^7 chord in the upper register. The voicing used for this is an interesting one, since the lowest note in the chord is the B♭ rather than the root, which is at the top instead. I recommend that you fret this chord with the first finger on the B♭, the second on the E and the fourth on the C.

The final bar of this section ends with a repeated legato figure which again uses the blues scale. The remainder of the study consist of repeats of earlier sections.

This is a complex piece, which requires a lot from you in terms of technical competency. The usual advice stands: practice the individual parts slowly and out of time to begin with, then gradually work up to tempo using a metronome or drum machine before attempting to play along with the track.

Strumming chords on the bass

Sound Advice

This track was recorded using my GB Guitars Rumour 4-string bass, strung with new Dunlop Super Bright Steel Strings gauges 40-60-80-100. It was recorded direct using an Apogee Duet 2 and a small amount of compression was added digitally.

Recommended Listening

1. 'Count Zero' - Stuart Hamm

2. 'Sexually Active' - Stuart Hamm

3. 'The Urge' - Stuart Hamm

4. 'Love Games' - Level 42
   (Mark King on bass)

5. 'Almost There' - Level 42
   (Mark King on bass)

6. 'Mr. Pink' - Level 42
   (Mark King on bass)

7. 'Gadaffi Duck' - Mark King

8. 'Lacquer Head' - Primus
   (Les Claypool on bass)

9. 'Tommy the Cat' - Primus
   (Les Claypool on bass)

10. 'School Days' - Stanley Clarke

Slap Bass Study No. 2

Written by Stuart Clayton

ADVANCED STUDIES FOR BASS GUITAR

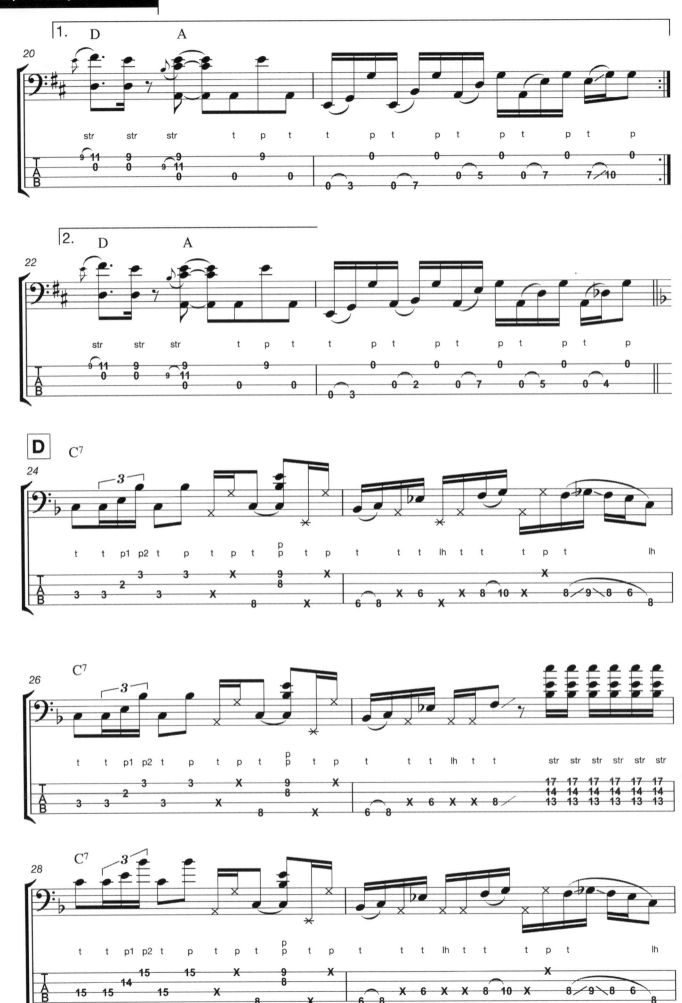

ADVANCED STUDIES FOR BASS GUITAR

D.S. al Coda

Two Handed Tapping Study

This piece was written back in 2003 and originally published in a book entitled *Giants of Bass.* **It's one of my favourite compositions, although I was never entirely happy with the middle section - including it here gave me the opportunity to rework it slightly. It's written very much in the style of bassist Stuart Hamm, who is arguably the most notable player to have used the two handed tapping technique for laying down accompaniment parts. Be sure to check out the songs in the recommended listening section at the end of these notes when working on this study.**

The opening A section is quite simple. In the first two bars, two chords are played: F#m7 and F△7. These chords share two common notes, the A and the E. In the F#m7 chord, the A is the minor third and the E is the flattened seventh. In F△7, the A is the major third and the E is the major seventh. As you'll hear, despite the presence of two common tones, these chords sound very different. I recommend that you tap the root-fifth figures in the fretting hand with the first and fourth fingers, using condensed fingering - this works best for most people as the fourth finger is typically stronger than the third. You'll want to play both notes with enough force to let them ring for the entire bar and therefore provide a solid base for the upper notes played by the picking hand. The most logical way to play the notes in the picking hand is to use the first and third fingers to play the A and E, then the first finger to play the slide from E to F#, the second to tap the A and the fourth for the E. These fingerings will also work for the F△7 and the G#m7 chord that finishes the section.

> ### TIP!
>
> *Although you do not necessarily need an understanding of music theory in order to compose good music, it can be extremely helpful. Understanding the way in which chords are constructed, as well as knowing which chords might go nicely togther is a huge help when writing music.*

At letter B the main accompaniment figure of the piece begins, in the key of C# minor. This is a four-bar part, with each bar featuring a simple melodic motif around F# - G# and C# at the eleventh fret position. In the first bar of the sequence (bar 6), play the C# and B in the fretting hand with the first and third

fingers respectively. In the picking hand, the opening notes should be played as follows: C# with the first finger, F# with the second, G# with the third. If you follow this fingering, the rest of the part should fall into place quite easily. The important thing here is that you allow all notes to ring into one another where possible - this will enhance the chordal nature of the part and is similar to the way a piano player would use a sustain pedal to thicken up the sound. Note that in the final bar of the sequence (bar 9), the low E is slapped with the thumb: let this note ring throughout the first three beats of the bar, but mute it for the final beat, where the chord changes to B/D#.

At letter C a new section begins based around a B minor chord. This figure is quite simple to play, although the interplay between the two hands might initially cause you a problem or two. In the fretting hand, tap the B with the first finger and use the third or fourth for both the F# and octave B. In the picking hand, the A and D at the twelfth fret can be tapped with the first and second fingers - the second can also play the C# and the first should be used for the slide upwards from A to B at the end of the first bar. In the second bar, the riff is repeated, but with a different, ear-grabbing chromatic tail to it: when playing the tenth chord that ends the phrase, tap the D at the tenth fret of the E-string with the first finger of the fretting hand and slide upwards to the F. Then tap the A at the fourteenth fret of the G-string with the first finger of the picking hand - both the F and A should now be ringing together as a double stop chord. Both notes are then moved downwards by one fret to become an E major chord. This is quite a striking sound and works very well in this piece which has so far been largely diatonic. This two-bar idea is played four times. This part is then played once again at letter E, following another reading of the earlier C# minor-based theme.

At letter F the middle section of the piece begins. The bass again plays an accompaniment figure here, heavily based on chord tones. For the F#m9 chord, tap the F# with the first finger of the fretting hand, and the C# and G# with the first and third fingers of the picking hand respectively. The F# at the eleventh fret of the G-string should be tapped with the second finger of the fretting hand - to play this note, your fretting hand will need to move back down the neck slightly, then back up. This note alternates with the A at the fourteenth fret of the

G-string. This tapping sequence is six semiquavers long, and is played twice, making twelve notes: the remaining four semiquavers in this bar follow the root-fifth-ninth shape already established, but the fifth (C#) follows the ninth (G#) at the end of the bar in order to allow the line to restart. The bar is played twice, then the chord changes to F△7, recalling the part from the Intro section. This four-bar sequence is then repeated. At bar 28, this part is embellished with some semiquaver triplet patterns. The first of these happens on the second half of the second beat: the root-fifth-ninth figure is played a triplet and is followed by two descending groups of three semiquavers and one descending semiquaver triplet at the end of the bar. This looks and sounds more complex than it is: your fingers will already be in place for the majority of these notes - the only finger which will need to move is the third finger of the fretting hand, which should be used for the C# and B notes on the G-string. The A on the G-string is best played with the second finger of the picking hand, as you have already been doing. Essentially, when playing this line, the fretting hand will need to 'duck under' the picking hand to tap the descending notes on the top string - this is shown in the photograph above. This idea is then repeated over the F△7 chord. At bar 34 the same idea is used for the G#m9 chord, although the top descending note is swapped for a low register G#. Only this note is played differently (with the first finger of the fretting hand) - the rest of this bar is played as before.

This part of the song ends with two chords - Aadd9 and Badd9 played using a very simple two handed voicing. These chords take us neatly back to C# minor for one final reading of the main theme. Follow the Dal Segno direction back to the sign at letter D (also marked letter G), and then jump to the Coda at the end of this part.

This piece is a lot simpler to perform that it might look or sound and is a great introduction to using the two handed tapping technique for playing accompaniment parts.

Sound Advice

I performed this piece using my Kubicki Ex-Factor bass - the same instrument that bassist Stuart Hamm used for many of the recordings included in the recommended listening list opposite. I used relatively new

strings for a brighter tone and recorded the bass direct. Compression and reverb were added digitally in order to give the part some extra presence.

Playing the intricate tapping part from bars 28 - 33

Recommended Listening

1. 'Flow My Tears' - Stuart Hamm

2. 'Surely the Best' - Stuart Hamm

3. 'Country Music' - Stuart Hamm

4. 'Moonlight Sonata' - Beethoven, (arranged for bass by Stuart Hamm)

5. 'Prelude in C' - Bach, arranged for bass by Stuart Hamm)

6. 'Terminal Beach' - Stuart Hamm

7. 'Wrong & Strong' - GHS (Stuart Hamm on bass)

8. 'NV43345' - Talas (Billy Sheehan on bass)

9. 'Accelerate' - Zander Zon

10. 'Sugar' - Michael Manring (from the *Bass Day 1998* DVD)

Two Handed Tapping Study

Written by Stuart Clayton

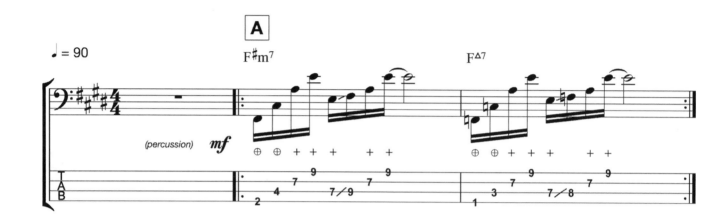

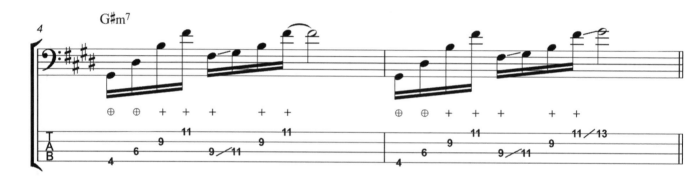

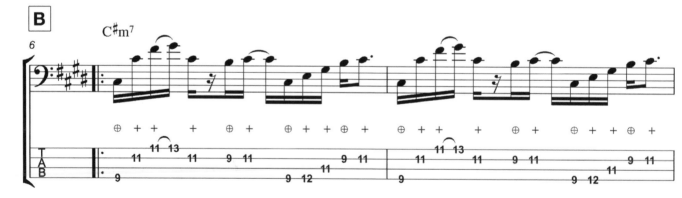

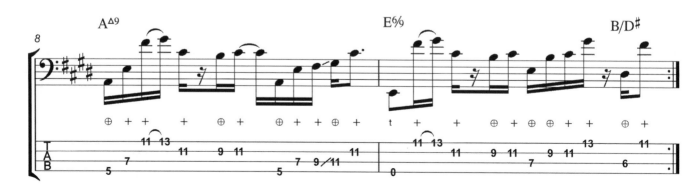

ADVANCED STUDIES FOR BASS GUITAR

ADVANCED STUDIES FOR BASS GUITAR

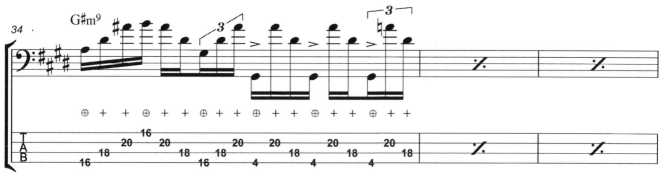

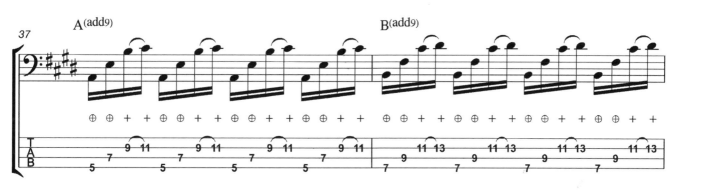

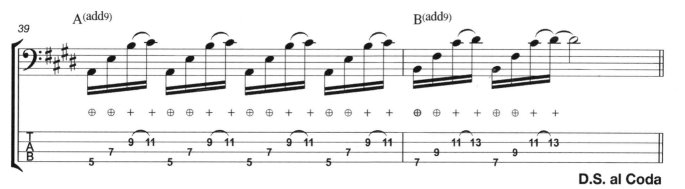

D.S. al Coda

Contemporary Techniques Study

This challenging piece was inspired by the work of virtuoso players such as Victor Wooten, Michael Manring and Jeff Schmidt, all of whom have been very successful in combining multiple techniques into one seamless performance. Consequently, this piece requires a solid grasp of a wide range of techniques such as slapping, strumming, tapping and palm muting.

The opening A section of this study is performed with the palm muting technique. The edge of the picking hand should be placed over the strings near the bridge to mute them, whilst notes are plucked with the thumb (not slapped), index and middle fingers. The majority of this line can be performed with the thumb in conjunction with the index finger, although there are a couple of places where the middle finger will be required. The first of these is the opening bar, which features a quick series of ghost notes played across the four strings after the initial open E. I recommend playing this phrase as follows: play the open E with the thumb, then immediately use the thumb again to play the ghost note on the A-string. The two ghost notes on the D and G-strings can then be performed with the index and middle fingers. The second ghost note on the D-string should be performed with the index finger.

The second part that requires clarification is the line in bar 4. After the open A-string is played with the thumb in the third beat, the fretting hand should hammer-on a D at the fifth fret of the A-string. This is then followed by ghost notes on the D and G-strings, played with the index and middle fingers respectively. This sequence is then repeated twice more, without the open A-string: the fretting hand hammers a pitched note and is followed by two ghost note plucks. All ghost notes here are played as demisemiquavers (thirty second notes), meaning that they will go by quite quickly. As the notes are ghost notes, this figure is purely a rhythmic decoration.

At letter B, the main theme of the piece is introduced - this section was inspired by the Michael Manring composition 'Excuse Me Mr. Manring'. The main idea behind this part is a slapped E on the first beat, followed by a series of ghost notes and a second low E, all on the second beat and all of which are performed using the double thumbing

technique. When playing this group of four notes, slap the E-string with the upper part of the thumb and allow it to come to rest on the A-string - don't bounce the thumb away as you would with conventional slap technique. You can then bring the thumb back upwards, playing the string on the way. This is essentially like using your thumb as a pick and is known as 'double thumbing.' The second half of the bar features a descending sequence of harmonics. These are played using conventional fingerstyle technique and should be allowed to ring into one another in order to create a chordal effect. In the following bar this sequence is replaced with two major ninth chords played as a combination of fretted notes and harmonics. These chords are very much a tip-of-the-hat to legendary bassist Jaco Pastorius, who used similar chords in his composition 'Portrait of Tracy'. This two bar section is played four times.

The C section of this piece is performed using slapping and strumming techniques and is a little more aggressive. Slap guides are written between the staves for guidance, although you'll need to ensure that you are comfortable strumming upwards and downwards to play this part. Many of the chords in this line are played in conjunction with open strings - you should allow all of the notes to ring into one another when playing this line. After this section the main theme returns (letter D) but is developed slightly: an $F^{\triangle 13}$ chord is added in place of the $G^{\triangle 9}$ in bar 19 and the section closes with a longer turnaround that features four different chords played as a combination of fretted notes and harmonics (bars 23 and 24).

At letter E a new part begins. Here, an $F^{\triangle 13}$ chord is played using the same voicing that was used back in bar 19. You should use the chordal fingerstyle technique to play this chord, switching to slap technique for the final F of the first beat. This F is followed by a fretting hand ghost note slap, after which another F is slapped. This is immediately followed by a double stop, tapped with the picking hand. The double stop is then repeated and pulled-off to sound the open D and G-strings. The fretting hand then hammers-on another double stop at the tenth fret. This is followed by a final double stop tapped by the picking hand. This is pulled off to sound the open A and D-strings, after which the fretting hand hammers-onto the G at the tenth fret of the A-string. The majority

ADVANCED STUDIES FOR BASS GUITAR

of the note choices in this part reflect the overall F△9 tonality. The second bar of this sequence is extended by two beats to be 6/4. The principles of performing it are exactly the same as the previous bar, but with added double stop taps and pull-off figures. After several repeats, this line segues nicely back into the main theme for one final time.

The final section of this piece - at letter G - is another slapped and strummed line, based on the earlier part from letter C. This time the line is extended into a four-bar part, with added chords that turn it around. As before, this section can be played louder and more aggressively than the previous part.

Have fun with this study - there's a lot to digest and it will require a lot from you in terms of technical skill. Whilst this piece is a great opportunity for you to put all of your techniques to the test, try to make the end result sound musical. Dynamics, phrasing and timing are all just as crucial to creating a captivating performance as techniques.

Sound Advice

On the recording of this piece I used my Zon Sonus 4-string bass. This instrument worked well for this piece as I have a 'ramp' installed between the two pickups, which makes performing the palm muting technique easier. This is because the ramp creates less string-to-body distance and therefore less room for your fingers to snag on the strings as you play. You don't need to install a ramp on your bass to play this piece and indeed, many great players don't bother with them. Players like Marcus Miller and Victor Wooten for example are masters of both palm muting and double thumbing, but do not use ramps.

In order to bring out the harmonics effectively, I favoured the bridge pickup slightly and boosted the midrange - you'll find it difficult to get the harmonics at the second the third frets to sound correctly without doing this. Whatever instrument you use to perform this piece, try to do the same. If you don't have a mid control on your bass, boost the midrange on your amp if you can. Some compression and reverb were added digitally - both of which are important when playing solo pieces of this nature.

An example of a ramp

TIP!

You can experiment with ramps by building your own out of cardboard. This will allow you to experiment with the size and shape that suits you best. Once you have something that works for you, a skilled luthier could build you one to match your instrument.

Recommended Listening

1. 'The Lesson' - Victor Wooten

2. 'Sex in a Pan' - Béla Fleck and the Flecktones (Victor Wooten on bass)

3. 'Portrait of Tracy' - Jaco Pastorius

4. 'School Days' - Stanley Clarke

5. 'Helios' - Michael Manring

6. 'Excuse Me Mr. Manring' - Michael Manring

7. 'Greetings, Earthlings!' - Michael Manring

8. 'Satori' - Jeff Schmidt

9. 'Mudita' - Jeff Schmidt

10. 'Numb' - Jeff Schmidt

Contemporary Techniques Study

Written by Stuart Clayton

ADVANCED STUDIES FOR BASS GUITAR

ADVANCED STUDIES FOR BASS GUITAR

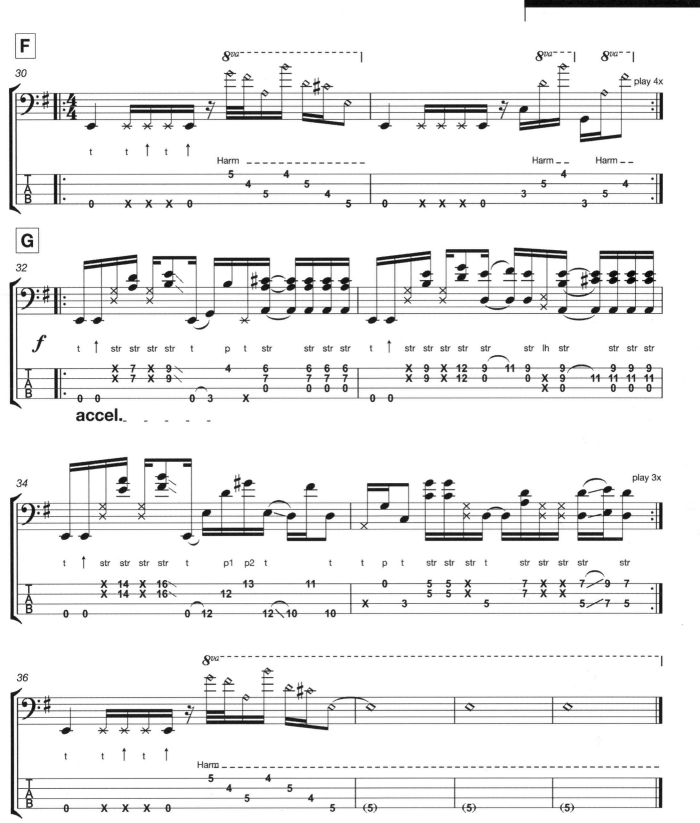